The Biochemistry of Genetics

The Biochemistry of Genetics

BY

J. B. S. HALDANE

F.R.S.

LONDON: GEORGE ALLEN & UNWIN LTD
NEW YORK: THE MACMILLAN COMPANY

FIRST PUBLISHED IN 1954
SECOND IMPRESSION 1956
THIRD IMPRESSION 1960

PRINTED IN GREAT BRITAIN
in 10 *point Times Roman type*
BY BILLING AND SONS LTD
GUILDFORD AND LONDON

Preface

This book is emphatically not a textbook. It is intended to summarize some of the main facts concerning a branch of science which is growing so rapidly that, had the book been up to date when it was written, it would have been out of date at the time of publication. I have chosen certain examples from the mass of published work, and doubtless neglected others of equal or greater importance, sometimes through ignorance, sometimes through faulty judgement. The only alternative would have been to fill several volumes. Nevertheless, there may be some advantage in trying to survey the whole field of the biochemical genetics of unicellular organisms, fungi, higher plants, and animals in a short book. Each group is well adapted for the study of some topics, and ill adapted for that of others. So a bird's eye view may gain in balance what it lacks in precision.

A few topics are in such a state of flux that I have considered it useless to give more than a small selection from the mass of apparently conflicting data, and even so may have added to the confusion by my discussions of them. These are the induction of mutation, the problem of multiple allelomorphism, and the problem of training and its transfer from one cell, or even one higher plant or animal, to another. The last of these problems has, unfortunately, been mixed up with politics in recent years. But in England we are lucky in having Hinshelwood and his colleagues, who share many, but not all, the views of Lysenko on this matter, and whose work can be appraised without linguistic difficulties on the one hand, or extraneous emotion on the other.

The book is based on lectures given in the Department of Biochemistry, University College, London, in 1950 and 1952. It is thus aimed at biochemists rather than geneticists, and I fear that most geneticists who may wish to read it will require an elementary textbook of biochemistry to assist them. Four other works give a number of relevant facts which I have omitted or at best condensed: *Unités biologiques douées de continuité génétique*, Catcheside's (1949) *The Genetics of Micro-organisms*, Harris's (1953) *An Introduction to Human Biochemical Genetics*, and Pontecorvo and his colleagues'

(1952) *The Genetics of Aspergillus nidulans.* I am particularly grateful to both Drs. Harris and Pontecorvo for allowing me to see their works in typescript, and for discussions which I have found most helpful, even where I differed from their conclusions. I have deliberately lightened my bibliography and perhaps unduly condensed my account of human biochemical genetics by reference to Harris's monograph. Similarly, I hope that Professor Ephrussi will excuse my inadequate account of his work on the ground that his Withering Lectures delivered at Birmingham University are in the press, and should be published before this book. Pontecorvo's excellent review only came into my hands after the first draft of this book was written. It clearly anticipates some of my conclusions.

I have attempted to present a picture of the living cell as it appears to one who has some acquaintance both with biochemistry and genetics. Such a picture must be speculative, and incorrect in many details. At best it may possess a certain heuristic value as presenting hypotheses whose proof or disproof would equally constitute an advance in biology. If some details are my own, it would be ungrateful to attempt to conceal how much it owes both to the published work and the even more stimulating, because less cautious, conversations both of my seniors, such as Bateson, Punnett, Garrod, Stephenson, and above all Hopkins and my father, and of my juniors, such as McIlwain, Quastel, Baldwin, Knight, Harris, Callan, and Pontecorvo.

J. B. S. H.

August 1952

Contents

Contents

CHAPTER I

The Elements of Genetics

This book is written for biochemists rather than for geneticists. I therefore begin by explaining some elementary genetical notions. I shall assume an elementary knowledge of biochemistry, for example the structural formulae of the amino-acids. However, for the benefit of readers who are geneticists rather than biochemists I have given a few formulae in the Appendix. Genetics is concerned with differences between similar organisms, and mainly with those differences which are not due to causes acting during the lifetime of the organisms concerned. This distinction works fairly well for higher organisms, but breaks down completely for unicellular organisms. If a cell can divide once an hour, but takes a day to adapt itself to ferment a type of sugar to which it is unaccustomed, a growing population can only adapt if the adaptation (and even the beginning of the adaptive process) is inherited. In such cases special experiments are needed to distinguish between the effects of adaptation and selection. On the other hand, there is much less carry-over of this kind in higher organisms, where only a very small fraction of the matter in any individual is derived from its parents, and adaptations are carried out or lost in a small fraction of the life cycle.

An example will show the kind of distinction which we can make in Metazoa. A straight-legged bitch produces a puppy with bent legs. This may happen for at least two reasons. The puppy may have been short of Vitamin D, and developed rickets, or its father may have been a dachshund. If the father had bent legs from rickets, this appears to have no effect on his progeny. If the mother were rickety, rickets may appear in her offspring because the blood with which she perfused the foetal placenta or the milk which she gave to the suckling was short of Vitamin D. It is particularly hard to draw a sharp line when we are dealing with virus infections.

If we consider any quantitative character, for example the height of a man, the milk yield of a cow during her first lactation, or the sucrose content of a sugar beet, we shall generally find that it is affected by differences both of what Galton called Nature and what he called Nurture. Roughly speaking, Nature covers all causes acting before fertilization, and Nurture all causes acting after it. In such a case we find our analysis much easier if we can keep one variable nearly constant, while allowing the other to vary, as when we deduce Boyle's and Charles's Laws by keeping first the temperature and then the pressure of a gas constant. We keep the nurture of a group of organisms nearly constant by supplying them all with the same food, water, light, infections, and so on.

There are three different ways of obtaining a population with nearly constant nature (apart from sex differences and the corresponding differences in most self-sterile hermaphrodites). The three types of population are:

1. A Clone, that is to say a population derived from a single cell by a series of mitotic divisions; for example a named variety of apple or potato, a group of aphids derived from one mother by parthenogenesis, or a pair of human monozygotic twins. Any culture of a haploid organism, such as all or almost all bacteria, and many fungi, is necessarily a clone, unless conjugation occurs within it, and even so the haploids derived from such a conjugation normally have the characters of the original clone.

2. A Pure Line, that is to say a population derived from a single individual or pair by prolonged self-fertilization or brother-sister mating. Examples are named varieties of wheat or peas, and a few lines of mice, guinea pigs, and Drosophila. One self-fertilization of a haploid, e.g. a fern prothallium, will give a pure line.

3. The first cross (but not later generations) between two pure lines.

The proof that they are genetically homogeneous is that selection within them is ineffective. You will readily get heavy or light mice by breeding from the heaviest or lightest members of a mixed stock. You will not do so by selecting within a pure line. Nevertheless, complete genetical homogeneity is an unattainable ideal like chemical purity, if only as a result of mutation; and pure lines are apt to be weak and sterile. A pure line of cows would be as useless for most practical purposes as a bar of pure iron. Both could be very useful for research. The reasons for the genetical homogeneity of such stocks are given in any textbook of genetics.

But apart from pure lines we can readily get stocks which breed true for a particular character or group of characters, say long-haired blue cats, or peas containing stachyose instead of starch, and with white instead of purple flowers. Genetics is based on the experimental crossing of such stocks and the analysis of later generations. Geneticists naturally tend to choose for their studies characters which are little affected by the environment. This is as inevitable as the choice by chemists for their preliminary studies of stable inorganic substances rather than metastable organic compounds, or free atoms or radicals. But it is unfortunate for two reasons. Economically important innate characters are generally capacities for response to suitable environments. A good dairy cow is one which produces a lot of milk on an English meadow, but will not do so on a Welsh mountain. The mountain cow is less variable in her response. Secondly, we can learn a great deal about physiological genetics by altering the environment, for example by showing that a particular line of yeast will only divide when grown in presence of thiamine, or can ferment glucose but not maltose.

Nevertheless, we begin with characters little affected by the environment. The sort of result which we get depends on whether we study characters manifested in haploids or diploids, that is to say organisms with one or two sets of chromosomes per cell. I shall not consider the complications introduced by polyploidy, although this is by no means confined to higher plants, as is sometimes supposed. Many normal mammals, including men, have tetraploid liver cells.

In most organisms with sexual reproduction there is a haploid phase with n chromosomes A B C D ... Two haploid gametes fuse to give a diploid phase with 2n chromosomes AA, BB, CC, DD ..., though sometimes sex is determined by a difference in one chromosome pair. In some organisms, such as many Ascomycetes, the diploid phase only lasts for a short time, and we usually study haploids. In others, such as most higher animals or plants, the haploid phase lasts for a short time. We do not study differences between spermatozoa, or eggs after the extrusion of the second polar body, though we can do a little with pollen grains and tubes. In other organisms, such as yeasts, seaweeds, mosses, and bees, we can study both haploids and diploids. We sometimes, particularly in plants, find a character which is cytoplasmically determined (cf. Chapter VII), but such characters are not very common, and in most organisms nuclear determination is much more important. That is why I have emphasized the chromosomal constitution.

Consider an organism in which the haploid phase is studied, such as one of the mould species *Neurospora crassa* and *N. sitophila*, or their hybrids. On crossing a normal (P) and a pale (p) stock, we can isolate single asci, dissect them, grow the eight spores in an ascus, and note the colour of the eight haploid cultures so produced. Here the first two divisions are meiotic, the third mitotic. The spores are arranged in a row in the ascus, and we get such orders as PPppPPpp or ppppPPPP. P and p only segregate at the first two divisions, and there are almost always just four P and four p spores. About once in five hundred asci something goes wrong with the meiosis, and we get less than eight, or unequal numbers. We say that P and p are genes, that is to say, structures which are reproduced (or copied) at each mitotic nuclear division, and which segregate regularly in the meiosis of heterozygous diploids. A segregating diploid such as Pp is called a heterozygote, a non-segregating diploid such as PP or pp a homozygote.

If we study the diploid phase we soon find that reciprocal crosses (♀A × ♂B and ♀B × ♂A) usually give the same result, which at once suggests nuclear rather than cytoplasmic determination. Sometimes the heterozygote is intermediate between the two homozygotes. For example, in *Primula sinensis* a pink-centred white form ("Duchess") and a dark red ("Crimson King") breed true. On crossing them we get a pinkish flower ("General Buller"). If the first is called DD, the second dd and the hybrid Dd, we have the situation shown in Table 1.

TABLE 1

Parents	Gametes	Zygotes		
DD × DD	D × D	DD		
dd × dd	d × d			dd
DD × dd	D × d			
(or dd × DD)			Dd	
DD × Dd				
(or Dd × DD)	D × (D + d)	½DD	½Dd	
dd × Dd				
(or Dd × dd)	d × (D + d)		½Dd	½dd
Dd × Dd	(D + d) × (D + d)	¼DD	½Dd	¼dd

There was a fairly good approximation to the expected ratios (de Winton and Haldane, 1933), but they are rarely fitted exactly, for three reasons. First, we cannot in practice use all the pollen grains produced by a single anther, as we can sometimes germinate all the spores in an ascus. And we can only use one of the four haploid nuclei produced in a female meiosis. So our numbers are subject to sampling errors. Second, there is some natural selection, both between pollen tubes and among young plants, favouring one type at the expense of another. Third, mutations occur, though we might have to grow several million plants before we found one affecting the gene in question.

Very commonly we find dominance. If we cross a homozygous tabby (AA)* with a black (aa) cat, all the kittens are tabby (Aa). Tabby is said to be dominant to black, and black recessive to tabby. Heterozygous (Aa) tabbies give equal numbers of Aa and aa when mated to blacks (aa). In other words, we cannot distinguish between AA and Aa cats except by breeding. One A gene can do the work of two as regards pigmentation. It is clear that recessives will breed true, while dominants may or may not do so.

However, dominance is a subjective matter. A suitable test may distinguish the two kinds of dominant. Sawin and Glick (1943) found that while the serum of most rabbits contains an atropine-esterase, some lack it. The lack is recessive. When they estimated the amount of the enzyme in the serum they found:

In 4 homozygotes, 232–348 units, average 271;
In 25 heterozygotes, 52–174 units, average 107.

It appears that the homozygotes make about twice as much enzyme as the heterozygotes, and that, in fact, the recessive gene is inactive, and each dominant acts nearly or quite independently. It is not very rare to find that colour develops rather more quickly in a homozygous than in a heterozygous dominant, even though the final stages of development are indistinguishable. This can only happen if the gene in question controls one of the slowest stages in the biochemical process concerned, and this acts as a limiting factor. It is often, but by no means always, the case that genes normally found in a species (often called wild type genes) are dominant over those which arise by mutation (mutant genes). In Drosophila it is sometimes possible to introduce more than two of these recessive mutant genes into a single cell by the use of chromosome fragments. Sometimes three or four have no more effect than two, in which case it is concluded that the recessive gene is inactive. Sometimes they produce a fly more like the wild type, and it is concluded that they are performing the function of the normal gene, but less intensely. In such cases dominance simply means that the normal gene has a factor of safety of 2 or more, just as a man can in most circumstances get on perfectly well with only one kidney or adrenal, and a blood analysis would not reveal the absence of the other.

* Dominant genes are commonly denoted by capital letters, recessives by small letters. Sometimes, however, the "wild type" gene is denoted by +, the mutant gene by a letter. Thus AA, Aa and aa cats can be denoted by $\frac{+}{+}$, $\frac{+}{a}$, and $\frac{a}{a}$.

When a double heterozygote segregates for two pairs of genes they usually segregate independently. Thus on crossing a homozygous coloured short-haired rabbit (CCLL) with a white long-haired (ccll) we get CcLl (coloured short-haired) progeny. On crossing these to ccll we get about equal numbers of CcLl, Ccll, ccLl, and ccll, showing that CL, Cl, cL and cl gametes are formed in roughly equal numbers.

Fat colour in rabbits is also genetically determined. Most rabbits have white fat. Others have yellow fat provided they are fed on green leaves or other food containing xanthophyll, but not if they are given a diet lacking xanthophyll, such as turnips. These rabbits lack a xanthophyll oxidase present in the normal animals, and provided the diet contains xanthophyll, yellow fat is a good recessive, due to a gene x. If we cross homozygous coloured white-fatted (CCXX) rabbits with white yellow-fatted (ccxx) the progeny are coloured white-fatted (CcXx) double heterozygotes. Crossed with ccxx they give about

$$86 \text{ CX}: 14 \text{ Cx}: 14 \text{ cX}: 86 \text{ cx}.$$

Such heterozygotes are called $\dfrac{\text{CX}}{\text{cx}}$ or $\dfrac{++}{\iota\text{X}}$. If we make up CcXx rabbits from the cross CCxx $\times$ ccXX we get $\dfrac{\text{Cx}}{\text{cX}}$ or $\dfrac{+\text{x}}{\text{c}+}$ double heterozygotes. Mated to ccxx they give about:

$$14 \text{ CX}: 86 \text{ Cx}: 86 \text{ cX}: 14 \text{ cx}.$$

This kind of geometrical isomerism is called linkage. It has been shown in several animal and plant species to be due to the position of the genes on the chromosomes. Genes which are near together tend to be strongly linked. The simplest proof of this arises from the fact that a few genes are visible, some mutants being deficiencies of a small section of a chromosome, others being duplications. They are found where they should be found according to maps constructed on the basis of linkage data. Most genes are, however, invisible with a microscope, though the electron microscope may yet reveal some of them.

Genes are generally reproduced accurately at a nuclear division, that is to say an A gives two A's, and an a two a's. If the accuracy were not very great, selection would be effective within pure lines. If it were always accurate a species could only try out combinations of pre-existing genes, and evolution could not have occurred. In fact genes do not always reproduce their like. The process of alteration is called mutation. It may be due to an alteration in a gene between nuclear divisions, or to an incorrect copying. It occurs with a frequency which is often of the order of 10^{-6} to 10^{-8} per cell division, but may be as high as 10^{-3}. It is worth remembering that a man has about 2^{48} cells, a Drosophila about 2^{24}, so that there are 48 or 24 divisions between an egg and an average somatic cell. The number of cell divisions in the male germ line is somewhat more than this, in the female line somewhat less, so the mutation rate per generation is often of the order of 10^{-5} or 10^{-6}.

We can then frame the working hypothesis that a gene is an organ in a particular region on a particular chromosome, with a definite function, and reproduced with great, but not complete, accuracy at each cell division. Experiments where mutation is provoked by X-rays (cf. Lea, 1946) (a method which gives molecular weights of the right order when applied to enzymes) strongly suggest that genes commonly have a molecular weight of the order of 10^6, or a diameter of 40–100 Å (cf. Haldane, 1920). The dimensions of the chromosomes, and the probable number of genes in them, suggest a similar figure.

We can now ask four questions concerning genes. Most of the rest of this book is an attempt to answer them. It will be seen to be a very inadequate attempt.

1. What do genes do? That is to say, what are the differences in biochemistry, in physiology, in development, in behaviour, between organisms with different sets of genes? This is a question analogous to that asked by physiologists concerning the function of an organ. We can state the functions of the heart or kidney with great accuracy without knowing how they are performed. For example, we need not know whether adenosine-triphosphate is concerned in contraction or relaxation, whether sugar is reabsorbed by the tubules by the same mechanisms as potassium; but an answer at this level would give us a new cellular physiology and biochemistry, a new embryology, a new psychology, and a new theory of evolution.

2. How do genes do what they do? Does each gene synthesize a specific substance, for example an antigen or an enzyme? Can genes be regarded as enzymes bound to the nuclear structure?

3. What are genes biochemically? Are they, perhaps, desoxyribo-nucleoproteins as all enzymes seem to be proteins?

4. How are genes reproduced and how is their process of reproduction sometimes altered so as to give a gene of a new type? Are such changes bound up with their functional activity?

Perhaps I am partly responsible (Haldane, 1920) for the suggested answer to question (2), namely that a gene makes a particular chemical species of enzyme or antigen, though if so I owe the idea to Cuénot (1903).* If this answer is correct it would not, of course, follow that all antigens or all enzymes were direct gene products. However, I doubt if the answer is correct. It is probably true sometimes, and is a useful working hypothesis because it is a guide to experiment, and a sufficiently clear statement to be capable of disproof if untrue.

Two simple answers to question (3) are possible. One is that genes are nucleoproteins like molecular viruses, copied by the rest of the cell by the same (unknown) process. The other is that they are similar to their primary product: the copying process is going on all the time, and most of the copies diffuse out into the cytoplasm, but one in each cell cycle is anchored to a chromosome. This has the merit of reducing the number of genic properties requiring explanation, but is probably incorrect.

If one is convinced by the arguments of Schrödinger (1944), as I am not, the answer to (4) is the answer to "What is life?" If one is convinced by those of Lysenko (1949), as again I am not, mutation is a highly adaptive process. To doubt their cogency is not to say that it is never adaptive. At the present moment geneticists, according to their geographical location, are likely to obtain promotion, or at least to escape dismissal, either by saying "Lysenko is always right" or "Lysenko is always wrong." The history of science renders it highly improbable that either of these statements is correct.

Before we try to answer even the first question we must say a little more about general genetics. In the first few years of Mendelism

* Since various claims have been made, particularly in America, for priority as to the hypothesis that genes make enzymes, it may be worth while quoting Cuénot *verbatim*. He makes it clear that he is enunciating a hypothesis. "Le plasma germinatif d'une souris grise doit contenir en puissance les trois substances qui, par leurs réactions réciproques, produiront plus tard les dépôts pigmentaires des poils; et sans doute ces trois substances sont contenues à l'état potentiel dans autant de particules matérielles de plasma germinatif (particules représentatives ou substances qualitatives de l'œuf = *mnémons*)." The grey mouse contains mnemons for a chromogen and for two enzymes forming black and yellow pigment respectively from it. The black mouse lacks the mnemon for the yellow-forming enzyme. The albino lacks that for the chromogen, but may or may not carry that for the yellow-forming enzyme. From a modern point of view the notion of a particle containing a substance in a potential state appears Aristotelian or at best Thomistic. Such a phrase as "is responsible for the synthesis of" may appear equally vague and anthropomorphic in A.D. 2003.

The term mnemon is due to Coutagne (1902). It might well have been used as we now use the word "gene." I suggest that, with its connotation of memory, it should be resurrected and used for particles evoked by a stimulus and capable of a limited amount of reproduction (cf. Chapter 7).

people wrote of factors for unit characters. E.g. the presence of hairs in *Matthiola incana* is dominant over their absence. So authors wrote of hairiness as a unit character due to a gene H. But it soon turned out that there were several different recessive hairless forms. $H_1H_1h_2h_2$ is hairless (glabrous). So is $h_1h_1H_2H_2$. On crossing we get $H_1h_1H_2h_2$, which is hairy and gives $\frac{7}{16}$ hairless offspring. One cannot specify a unit character controlled by H_1 and another by H_2. Further work showed that one of the genes needed for anthocyanin production was also needed for hair formation. Recently, however, a series of unit characters in the old sense has been discovered. These are the antigens described in the next chapter.

The next hypothesis was that each gene controlled a unit process (Haldane, 1941) presumably capable of description in biochemical terms, which might, however, play a part in several developmental processes. We shall see that this process, e.g. a particular dehydrogenation, is sometimes known. In other cases it is not. Thus white cats are generally deaf. Mice with a particular type of microcytic anaemia due to a recessive gene usually have a flexed tail and a white spot on the belly. It is anybody's guess what is the common link in the three developmental processes concerned. Such action of a single gene on very different characters is called pleiotropism. Grüneberg (1947) maintains that there must be a common biochemical process. It is perhaps not inconceivable that a single gene may have functions as different as the secretory and storage functions of the liver, the anti-diuretic and uterine stimulating functions of the posterior pituitary, or the two catalytic functions of xanthine oxidase; but Grüneberg is probably correct in most cases.

A large fraction, perhaps a majority, of all mutants are lethal, that is to say the homozygote dies, while the heterozygote may or may not be discernible. The homozygote may die at an early stage from unknown causes, like the homozygous yellow mouse which dies at the eight-cell stage, or at a late stage from obvious reasons, like the homozygous black-eyed white mouse, which dies of anaemia in its first day or two of post-natal life unless kept alive by trans-fusion. If, as in this case, we can preserve the life of a lethal homozygote, we know, at least from an operational point of view, what is wrong with it. If, as in the case of human amaurotic idiocies, where there is certainly an anomaly of lipoid metabolism, we cannot do so, we have a good deal less knowledge. In general we cannot keep lethal homozygotes of higher plants and animals alive, though chlorophyll-less mutants of green plants will often live on sugar solution. In lower plants this is often possible with types which are

B

lethal in the normal environment. These are called auxotrophs, and are lethal because a particular synthetic capacity has been lost, but live normally, or nearly so, when supplied with the missing metabolite. I deal with such genes in Chapter III.

One point about polyploidy is of biochemical importance. We might expect that a cell with three, four, or more sets of chromosomes would differ greatly in its physiology from one with only two, as all kinds of biochemical processes would be proceeding at more than the normal rate. This is not the case. The differences are usually slight. Sometimes a tetraploid cell is about twice the volume of a diploid, so we can suppose that cytoplasmic as well as nuclear processes are going on at twice the normal rate. But the cell size is not invariably proportional to the chromosome number. On the other hand, if one chromosome is present in triplicate or only once, i.e. the nucleus can be represented as

$$A B C D \ldots \quad A B C D \ldots \quad A B C D \ldots$$
$$A B C D \ldots \text{or} \quad B C D \ldots \text{instead of } A B C D \ldots$$
$$A$$

the organism is often inviable, and almost always abnormal. An exception to this rule is given by the sex-determining X chromosome. Thus the whole set of chromosomes is responsible for a quantitatively balanced system of reactions, and the X chromosome for a similarly balanced subset.

I have not referred to the special genetical methods and criteria employed in human genetics. An account of some of them is given by Haldane (1948) and Harris (1953). For example, a rare condition found among the children of normal parents can only be due to an autosomal recessive gene if it is commoner among the children of married pairs of first cousins than in other families.

In conclusion, I shall define a few words. If two or more genes, like A and a, X and x, and so on, have the property that only one can get into a gamete, they are said to be allelomorphs (in America allels). If there are more than two they are called multiple allelomorphs. They are said to occur at the same locus on a chromosome. A gene located on an X or sex-determining chromosome, of which women and cocks have two and men and hens one, is called sex-linked. One located elsewhere is called autosomal.

CHAPTER II

Possible Primary Products of Gene Action

Of all the characters which have been studied, those whose genetics are simplest are the antigens for which man, and perhaps all species of mammals and birds, are polymorphic. We will begin with a very simple example. If we inject human blood corpuscles from a particular man A into a rabbit, the rabbit develops antibodies, and its serum will often agglutinate all human blood corpuscles. If we exhaust it with the corpuscles of A, that is to say make it agglutinate several batches of them, it will finally lose all its anti-human agglutinins. But if we exhaust it with the corpuscles of another man B, it will finally cease to agglutinate them, but may still agglutinate the corpuscles of A. In this way we can produce a rabbit serum which agglutinates the corpuscles of about three-quarters of the human race, who are said to carry the agglutinogen M. Similarly an agglutinogen N can be detected. Sometimes we may hit on a rabbit which produces very little anti-human antibody except anti-M or anti-N. These agglutinogens are determined by two allelomorphic genes L^M and L^N. Every human gamete carries one or other of them.* All human beings are of the genotype:

$L^M L^M$, with the M agglutinogen on the corpuscles;
$L^M L^N$, with the M and N agglutinogens on the corpuscles;
or $L^N L^N$, with the N agglutinogen on the corpuscles.

Thus no one can have the M agglutinogen unless one or both parents had it, and similarly with the N. Further, no treatment has ever led to the appearance or disappearance of either of these substances. They appear to depend wholly on nature, and not at all on nurture. No nurtural difference will as yet abolish either of them without killing the person concerned. Further, since there is no case not explicable by illegitimacy where two parents without M produced (or are alleged to have produced) a child with it, we can

* Or perhaps life is impossible without one or other of them.

say with great confidence that only one gene is concerned. This ‛
not generally the case for characters other than antigens. The compresence of several genes is needed to produce colour in a mouse hair
or a Drosophila eye, to produce a full coat of hair on a mouse, or
wings (other than barely visible vestiges) on a Drosophila, and so on.
Where only one such gene is known to be needed in a species, we
have good reason to believe that further research would reveal
others. (Thus two genes are needed for anthocyanin production in
Lathyrus odoratus, so far only one in the related *Pisum sativum*.)

What is more, this is a very general (though not quite universal)
property of corpuscular antigens. Todd (1930) immunized one fowl
(*Gallus domesticus*) with the blood of a large number of others.
Its serum would agglutinate the corpuscles of all other fowls. If
exhausted with the corpuscles of A it would still agglutinate those of
B, C, etc., even if they were brothers and sisters of A. But if exhausted
with the corpuscles of any cock and hen, it would not agglutinate
the corpuscles of any of their progeny. Thus no fowl has corpuscular
antigens not found on the corpuscles of one of its parents. The same
holds (so far with one exception) for human beings. Since a great
many different antigens are known, each determined by a single gene,
this means that each is determined by that one gene and not (like an
anthocyanin or a melanin) by the interaction of several genes. This
conclusion is probably false in the formal sense. If an antigen is made
in part, say, from galactose molecules, it requires its own special
gene, and also genes concerned in making galactose from other
sugars; but these latter are presumably vital, in the sense that their
absence is incompatible with life.

However, even when antigens obey Todd's law this does not
mean that all the genes are acting independently. For example, in
members of the human group AB which carry both the A and B
antigens on the corpuscles, the amount of A is often a good deal
less than in people who have one A gene and one recessive (O) gene.
This may be due to competition either for substrate from which to
synthesize the haptenes, or for proteins to which to attach them.
Similarly there is a good deal more of the H antigen in group O
than in other groups. It seems that there is competition between the
A and B genes and some other "organ," probably *not* the recessive
O gene. The amount of both M and N antigens in heterozygotes is
about half what it is in homozygotes, which could be true either if
the two allelomorphs were acting independently, or if they were
competing for a limited amount of substrate or of space.

Let us now consider some exceptions to Todd's law. The Lewis[a] and Lewis[b] antigens are due to allelomorphic genes. There is, perhaps, a rare third gene giving Lewis[c]. Homozygotes for the Le[a] gene react with anti-Le[a] serum throughout life. Heterozygotes only do so in the first eighteen months or so of life, though at least some of them excrete it without having detectable amounts in their corpuscles. Such competition between allelomorphs, or antimorphism, is known in other fields of genetics. To get the Le[a] antigen in an adult one must have two like Le[a] genes. There is no question of two unlike genes co-operating to make it.

On the other hand, Irwin (1947) found that hybrids between several species of dove and pigeon had corpuscular antigens which were not present in either parent species, along with all the antigens of both parents. Of course the genes were in a very abnormal environment. This observation is a conclusive disproof of the hypothesis that a particular type of gene always makes a particular type of antigen, and that no antigens are made otherwise. Nevertheless, that hypothesis is sufficiently often true to be of value in prediction.

The chemical nature of some of the genetically determined antigens is known. Morgan (1950), and Annison and Morgan (1952) give numerous references.

The specific components (haptenes) are mucoids of molecular weight about 250,000, which can be obtained from ovarian cysts in large quantities of the order of 300 gm. They differ in their optical rotatory powers. The following are examples:

$$\begin{array}{cccc} & H & A(?\,A_1) & Le^a; \\ \alpha D & -35° & +15° & -45° \end{array}$$

They seem to be built up of four sugars, namely D-galactose, L-fucose, N-acetyl-D-glucosamine, and N-acetyl-D-chondrosamine, and eleven amino-acids, namely glycine, alanine, serine, threonine, valine, leucine, proline, aspartic and glutamic acids, lysine and arginine. L-fucose (6-desoxy-L-galactose) has also been found in seaweeds and the jelly of sea-urchin eggs. The percentages found are different, for example A substance contains 18% fucose, Le[a] only 13%; A contains about equal amounts of glucosamine and chondrosamine, Le[a] about three times as much of the former. Threonine appears to be the commonest amino-acid in each. It is greatly to be hoped that comparative biochemical work may be done on the products of two allelomorphic genes such as I[A] and I[B] or Le[a] and Le[b].

Le[a] has a very remarkable biological property. Grubb (1948) found that Le[a]Le[a] individuals produce saliva and other secretions containing the Le[a] substance and no other haptenes. Other people with about 1 % exceptions secrete the H substance, and also the A and B substances if they make them. Further, in the secretors the A, B, and H substances are present in a water-soluble form, while in the non-secretors they are only present in an alcohol-soluble form, as on the corpuscles. (Friedenreich and Hartmann, 1938.) Morgan's analyses are of the water-soluble form. Another surprising effect of an antigenic gene is that A_2 red corpuscles are less readily haemolyzed by hypotonic saline than A_1, O, or B (Schøne, 1944).

There is similar evidence that different types of haemoglobin are made by different allelomorphic genes. A gene si, which is not rare either in Africa or among American negroes, produces (in America, but not certainly in Africa) a fairly fatal anaemia where homozygous. The haemoglobin in the corpuscles of patients forms solid crystals or perhaps tactoids (Harris, 1950) on reduction, and distorts the corpuscles into shapes which have been compared to sickles. The sisi genotype is called sickle-cellanaemia. The heterozygotes Si si are fairly normal, but may sometimes have a slight anaemia. However, if their haemoglobin is completely reduced, some of the corpuscles are distorted, and the "sickle-cell trait," which is the name given to the heterozygous genotype, can be detected. It is very common throughout Africa south of the Sahara. Pauling, Itano, Sanger and Wells (1949) made the very remarkable discovery that the carboxyhaemoglobins and the reduced haemoglobins of normals and sickle-cell anaemics differ in their mobilities in an electric field, the latter being more basic, the isoelectric points differing by about 0·23 of a pH unit. Perutz and Mitchison (1950) found that the two oxyhaemoglobins have about the same solubility, but reduced sickle-cell haemoglobin is much less soluble than normal haemoglobin. The haem is certainly the same, so the difference must be in the globins. Everything would be explained if each molecule of sickle-cell haemoglobin contained two or three more lysine or arginine, or two or three less glutamic or aspartic acid residues. The analytical data of Schroeder, Kay and Wells (1950) show that they do not differ in this way, though they may contain more serine and threonine, less leucine and valine. More remarkably, Perutz, Liquori and Erich (1950) were quite unable to distinguish the X-ray diffraction patterns of the two haemoglobins.

So far as I know, nobody has made the experiments which would have been obvious thirty years ago, namely, to compare the oxygen and carbon monoxide dissociation curves of these haemoglobins and to measure their spectra as exactly as possible.

The matter was rapidly complicated by a series of further discoveries by Itano and Neel (1950) and Itano (1951). Families were discovered in which a child had a not very severe sickle cell anaemia, and only one parent had the sickle-cell trait. The other parent was found to have two electrolytically separable types of haemoglobin. One of them is normal haemoglobin. Of the new types one agrees with sickle-cell haemoglobin in its electrophoretic behaviour, but not its solubility; the other is even more electronegative, but soluble when reduced. It appears but is not conclusively proved that these are due to other allelomorphs at the same locus as the gene for sickle-cell anaemia. Finally, anaemics may have up to 25% of foetal haemoglobin. This forms 80% or more of the haemoglobin in normal babies at birth, and usually disappears at about four months. It can be distinguished by its high resistance to alkali denaturation, but has much the same solubility and electrophoretic mobility as normal haemoglobin. It is also found in several other types of anaemia, and its continued production may be regarded as an adaptive response. Table 2 summarizes the situation. Haemoglobins a, b, c, and d

TABLE 2
Types of Haemoglobin

	Normal	Sickle	Rare	Rare	Foetal	
	a	*b*	*c*	*d*	*f*	
Solubility when reduced	+	−	+	+	+	
Mobility at pH 6·5	+	++	+++	++	+	
Resistance to alkali	−	−	−	−	+	
Genotype—						Phenotype—
SiSi	100	0	0	0	0	Normal
Sisi	55–77	23–45	0	0	0	Sickle cell trait
sisi	0	75–100	0	0	0–25	Severe anaemia
Sisi^c	+	0	+	0	0	? normal
sisi^c	0	+	+	0	±	Moderate anaemia
Sisi^d	+	0	0	+	0	? normal
sisi^d	0	+	0	+	±	Moderate anaemia

appear to be produced by allelomorphic genes. It is not yet known why the mixture of b haemoglobin with c or d is less soluble than the mixture with a. Nor is it known whether cc and dd homozygotes are normal. The haemoglobin in some other congenital anaemias, for example thalassaemia (Cooley's anaemia) appears to be a mixture of normal (a) and foetal (f) haemoglobin, according to Rich (1952).

Thus the gene responsible for thalassaemia produces a chemical change, apparently by reducing the production of normal haemoglobin, the foetal being produced in adult life as a physiological compensation.

All these facts could be explained on the hypothesis that each of the four Si alleles manufactures its own type of globin independently of the others, except that there is a certain amount of competition, the normal allelomorph usually making rather more of the total than the sickle-cell haemoglobin-making gene. This hypothesis, which does not accord with the findings of Callan (cf. Chapter IX) on the permeability of nuclear membranes, has the merit of being disprovable.

Hörlein and Weber (1948) described a chronic congenital methaemoglobinaemia in which 15–25% of the haemoglobin was present as methaemoglobin, and this had a different absorption spectrum from normal methaemoglobin. By transferring the haem to normal globin and transferring normal haem to the globin derived from this methaemoglobin they showed that the haem was normal, and the globin abnormal. The "patients" were in good health, and did not respond, like the Irish cases described in Chapter VI (p. 80) to ascorbic acid or methylene blue. Moreover, the character was inherited as an autosomal dominant. It is probable, then, that like people with the sickle-cell trait, they have two different allelomorphic genes at some locus, each responsible for making a different globin. The homozygote for the mutant gene might make 100% methaemoglobin, and would presumably be lethal. Mutations of this type may, however, have had a great evolutionary importance, for example in originating new types of cytochrome. If globins are primary gene products, Hörlein and Weber's gene must be at the same locus as those described in Table 2. In the present state of our knowledge this hypothesis could only be verified by arranging a marriage between a member of this family and a person with sickle-cell anaemia, or at least heterozygous for si.

There is, however, a simpler way of solving the question. Douglas, Haldane, and Haldane (1912) found that when the haemoglobin of an individual was fully saturated with CO and O_2 the ratio of the affinities for these two gases was constant, and independent of pH, dilution, and so on. The ratio remained constant for a given individual over some years. For J. S. Haldane it was 300 : 1, for C. G. Douglas 246 : 1, for mice A, B, C, and D 167 : 1, 139 : 1, 222 : 1, and 150 : 1.

Barcroft (1928) and his colleagues showed that these differences also occur in rabbits and horses, as well as between species, and are highly correlated with differences between the positions of absorption bands in the spectra of oxyhaemoglobin and carboxyhaemoglobin. Fox (1945) found spectroscopic differences between the haemoglobins of different rabbits, but not between those of different frogs or earthworms, nor, curiously enough, of different men. Haldane and Priestley (1935) went so far as to state: "It does, in fact, appear to be fairly certain that each individual has a specific kind of haemoglobin just as he has a specific nose," and to cite Todd's results as an analogy. This may well be an exaggeration, but there are certainly many types of haemoglobin within a species. It is possible that they are all determined by genes at the same locus as that for the sickle-cell character and Hörlein and Weber's methaemoglobinaemia. If this is proved to be so it will be highly probable that haemoglobin is a primary product of genes at this locus. If, as I think more likely, several different loci are concerned, we shall either have to suppose that the haemoglobin molecule is made up of parts manufactured by several different genes, or that it is passed from one gene to another like a car along a conveyor belt, or to adopt some other such hypothesis of co-operation. Branson and Banks (1952) report the curious finding that the rate of turnover of phosphorus in erythrocytes, measured by radioactivity, is slightly lower in Sisi than in SiSi, and reduced to less than half in sisi. Since haemoglobin has not been thought to play any part in phosphorus metabolism this is completely unexplained.

Even if the hypothesis of the independent production of different molecules by different genes is confirmed at this level, it has been disproved at another level. Filitti–Wurmser, Jacquot–Armand, and Wurmser (1950) have done a large amount of quantitative work on the β, or the anti-B, iso-agglutinin of human group A bloods, and its combination with the B agglutinogen. To obtain reproducible results it is necessary first, by heating the serum to 56° C for 50 minutes, to destroy a thermolabile component of complement which partially inhibits agglutination. When this has been done, provided that a number of further precautions are taken, the results are extremely constant. Thus the ratio 2·54 given in Table 3, is the mean of twenty determinations on different sera with a standard deviation of 0·18, its own standard error being 0·04. This standard deviation includes both experimental errors and differences which may exist between individuals. One character studied was the ratio of the maximum number of corpuscles agglutinated at 4° C to the number agglutinated at 37° C when 0·6 ml of serum was added to

0·3 ml of a corpuscular suspension. The actual numbers were very variable, the most powerful serum agglutinating about ten times as many as the weakest. Another character measured was the enthalpy, $-\Delta H$, obtained by comparing the rates of change with concentration of the fraction of agglutinin fixed, at two temperatures.

TABLE 3

Measurable Characteristics of Human Isoagglutinins

Genotype	$N_4°/N_{37}°$	$-\Delta H$ cal.	M.W.
A_1A_1	1·40	8,000	
A_1O	2·54	16,000	$\sim 500,000$
A_2O	2·02	9,000	
A_3O	1·26	3,000	
OO	1·2	1,700	$\sim 170,000$

The molecular weight was determined by Wurmser, Filitti–Wurmser, and Aubel–Lesure (1952) with the ultracentrifuge. Table 3 only gives a few of the characteristics measured. The entropy of the system appears to diminish when agglutinin in OO sera combines with the B substance. It is suggested that this can be explained by a simultaneous change in the opposite direction, "a sort of reversible denaturation" in the remainder of the agglutinin molecule. But, however the measures are finally interpreted, the experimental data are definite and reproducible. They make it quite impossible that the agglutinin produced by A_1O persons should be a mixture of those produced by A_1A_1 and OO. This is also shown by the fact that when A_1O agglutinin is partially absorbed on corpuscles, the residue has exactly the same properties as the original substance. The difference of the molecular weights also shows that the agglutinins do not merely differ in respect of their specific groups.

We must, therefore, conclude that a heterozygous genotype, although it may make two different agglutinogens, makes a single agglutinin specific for it. The authors "think that the genes A and O, or genes closely linked to them, co-operate in an individual of genotype A_1O in the formation of anti-B isoagglutinin, imprinting the characteristic structure of $\beta(A_1O)$." This is almost certainly true, but the formation of agglutinin may be causally determined by the nature of the antigens present, these latter being the primary gene products. It must be remembered that we know nothing about the mechanism of the formation of isoagglutinins save that it is an exception to the general rules governing the formation of antibodies. However that may be, it has been shown that a heterozygote can produce a protein characteristic of it.

An interesting by-product of this work is the proof that, by the very delicate tests provided by the authors' technique, the B agglutinogens on BO and BA_1 corpuscles differ neither in quantity nor in any thermodynamically measurable characteristic. Additional support is, therefore, given to the hypothesis that the agglutinogens, though not the agglutinins, are primary gene products.

Another fairly clear case where a protein may be a primary gene product is haemophilia. Here the blood fails to coagulate because of the absence (? total) of a particular protein found in fraction I of the plasma along with fibrinogen and other substances readily precipitated by ethanol at $0°$ C (cf. Edsall, 1947).

Haemophilia is due, both in men and dogs, to a recessive sex-linked gene on the X chromosome, of which females have two, and males only one. A rare type of sub-haemophilia, in which the blood coagulates rather slowly, is due to a different change at the same locus. Haemophilia never occurs as the result of mutations on other chromosomes. The haemorrhagic diathesis caused by such changes can be distinguished from it. The simplest hypothesis is that this particular gene or short chromosomal section is concerned in making the protein, or a characteristic part of it, and in no other activity, and that no gene in another chromosome is so concerned. For if it were we should sometimes find autosomally inherited haemophilia. If other genes are concerned they would, perhaps, be concerned in making parts of several proteins, and a change in any of them would be lethal. Incidentally we can deduce that this gene has preserved its functional activity since the Palaeocene or more probably the late Cretaceous, when men and dogs had a common ancestor.

However, a consideration of the anterior pituitary should warn us against too simple a theory. An autosomal recessive in the mouse causes dwarfism which can be cured by anterior pituitary implants. It is still not quite clear which hormones are missing (cf. Grüneberg, 1952), but almost certainly more than one is absent or greatly reduced in amount. The histology of the anterior pituitary is grossly abnormal in these mutant mice, and it is probable that the complete or partial absence of several hormones is due to one primary chemical abnormality. The normal allelomorph of this gene is also of interest because, so far as we know, it only acts in the nuclei of anterior pituitary cells, though presumably present in every cell of the body.

The human blood groups were discovered because blood transfusions often led to serious consequences. The transplantation of other tissues in mammals is still more difficult. As a general rule a transplant from one individual to another fails, the graft being invaded by leucocytes from the host, and killed, even if it is replaced by host tissue. However, it is possible to transfer tissues between members of a pure line, and also into a member of a first cross between two pure lines from either of them. Little (1914) had investigated the genetics of transplantability of tumours in mice, and formulated the general law which has since been abundantly verified by himself and others, both for tumours and normal tissues of mice, and less conclusively of other mammals. The explanation of the facts which is generally accepted was given by Haldane (1933), but, like other simple theories, may not be universally true; though it certainly is so in some cases. Each of a fairly large number of genes in an individual makes a specific antigen. A graft containing any antigen "foreign" to the host is destroyed. Hence the graft must carry no foreign genes of this set. It follows that the F_1 between two pure lines can grow tissues from either of them, but not conversely. But in the F_2 only some members will carry all the genes derived from a particular parent. The number of loci at which pure lines of mice may differ in this important respect varies from one or two to over twelve. If it were infinite one could never transplant from one individual to another, and biochemical individuality would be something metaphysical. If it were very small, mice would fall into a few groups like the human blood groups.

This "intolerance," as Medawar calls it, is a very striking aspect of individuality in higher animals. The fact that it depends in a direct and simple manner on the genotype is equally striking. Unfortunately its biochemical basis is unknown. In a series of papers Gorer (especially 1938 and 1947) has dealt with the immunity reactions, and shown that some of the antigens are found on corpuscles. They *may* be biochemically like the human antigens investigated by Morgan. Medawar (e.g. 1953) and his colleagues have taken up the challenge, and have so far succeeded in reducing the intensity of the host's immunity reaction, though not as yet in abolishing it. It must, however, be realized that the difficulty of transplanting is only one indication of the immense biochemical diversity which exists within a species, and is, indeed, a prerequisite for evolution. It has the great advantage of being much more simply related to its genetic basis than other kinds of diversity, for example diversity in size or metabolic capacity.

CHAPTER III

Genes Controlling
Synthesis in Fungi

All normal stocks of *Neurospora crassa* grow on a "minimal medium" consisting of water, inorganic salts, including sulphate and nitrate, glucose, and a trace of biotin. They will grow somewhat better on the minimal medium plus yeast extract, malt, and autolyzed Neurospora mycelium; this is called the "complete medium." A large number of mutants will grow on the complete medium, but slowly or not at all on the minimal medium. These auxotrophic mutants may be called conditional lethals. Probably many of the metazoan lethals are conditional. Thus a lethal anaemic form of mouse can be kept alive by transfusion, a sterile dwarf form can be made to grow and the males rendered fertile by injecting anterior pituitary hormone, and so on. The use of Neurospora for biochemical purposes is largely due to Beadle, who has also summarized the earlier results (Beadle, 1945). Admirable accounts both of the genetics and much of the later biochemical work is given by Catcheside (1949) and Horowitz (1950). *Aspergillus nidulans* will grow on a minimal medium containing no organic substance but glucose, and with nitrate, sulphate, and phosphate, as N, S, and P sources (Pontecorvo *et al.*, 1952).

Mutation can be induced by treating the microconidia (uninucleate asexual reproductive cells) with X-rays, ultraviolet radiation, or chemical mutagens. These may produce up to 50% mutants, but only in doses which kill the majority of the spores. Several methods are available for picking out mutants in various fungi and bacteria. For example:

1. Isolated spores are grown on complete medium, and a subculture from each such culture transferred to minimal medium. Those whose subcultures fail to grow are kept. This is a laborious method.

2. Spores are sown on a minimal medium, and those which do not grow are picked out before they die.

3. Spores are grown on minimal medium and filtered after a few hours or days. The filter retains those which have grown hyphae.

4. Some bacteria (not Neurospora) are killed by penicillin only when growing. Minimal medium plus penicillin selects the mutants, which are then grown on complete medium without penicillin (Davis, 1948).

5. Aspergillus spores needing biotin generally die in a biotin-free medium in four days. Those needing biotin *and* thiazole or some other substance live longer. Thus of 4×10^6 untreated biotin-needing spores 52 survived for 147 hours. Of these 22 were further mutants, mostly requiring an amino-acid (Pontecorvo *et al.*, 1952). This is an observation of some evolutionary importance. Once a species has started on the path towards parasitism by losing some synthetic capacity, it may survive longer in an unfavourable medium if it has lost still other capacities, and is not, so to say, tempted to grow.

Having obtained a stock which grows on the complete but not the minimal medium two more steps must be taken. Their order is irrelevant. It must be established that the mutation is due to a single gene. This is done by crossing it to a normal stock and showing that just half the spores in each ascus resemble either parent. And the nature of its needs must be established. This is done in several steps. We can add a vitamin-free protein digest or a yeast extract to the minimal medium and see whether either of these will sustain growth. In fact, of course, a completely vitamin-free protein digest is not readily obtained. Table 4 shows the results of this type of analysis

TABLE 4

Need	Ophiostoma	Aspergillus	Penicillium
Amino-acids	178	40	250
Nucleic acid components ..	150	145	19
Vitamins	43	37	55
Reduced S	74	305	?
Reduced N	?	20	31
Total	445	547	355

for the fungi *Ophiostoma multiannulatum* (after Fries, 1947), *Aspergillus nidulans* (after Pontecorvo *et al.*, 1952), and *Penicillium notatum* (Bonner, 1946b). The former was grown in a minimal medium containing NH_4^+, the latter two in one containing NO_3^-. Bonner's technique did not enable him to distinguish between inability to reduce sulphate and to synthesize cysteine.

The most surprising feature is, perhaps, that over half the mutants in Aspergillus grow in presence of sulphide, cysteine, etc., but not of sulphate. In fact, 289 would grow on sulphite, and the other 16 on thiosulphate. This, however, does not imply that there are a great number of processes concerned in sulphate reduction. It is more probable that there is one which is particularly sensitive. Pontecorvo has also shown that the details of the process of selection make a great difference to the proportions of auxotrophic mutants of different types which are found. Nevertheless, real differences occur. Pontecorvo has failed to obtain inositol-requiring mutants in Aspergillus, though they are common in some other fungi.

The next step, if possible, is to make the nature of the requirement more precise, for example, to show that the mutant will grow in minimal medium plus arginine or riboflavin. Beadle's school denote a mutant whose growth is restored by arginine as "arginineless." This terminology has the merit of brevity, but it is unfortunate for two reasons. In the first place it suggests that these mutants lack arginine or that they cannot synthesize it. Secondly, it is ambiguous. If an "arginineless" mutant will grow on ornithine it might as well, or better, be called "ornithineless." Still another type of auxotrophic mutant is known, which will grow neither on the minimal nor the complete medium, but will grow on the minimal medium plus a supplement. For example, Pontecorvo was unable to obtain a "tryptophanless" mutant by his standard methods. He obtained one by sowing on minimal medium plus tryptophan, but its growth is inhibited by other amino-acids.

It is important that almost all mutants require a single supplement. Out of 612 listed by Pontecorvo, only 33 which would grow on complete but not on minimal medium have failed to respond to a single substance. They presumably include simultaneous mutants (e.g. thiamineless and lysineless), and mutants requiring supplements not available (e.g. perhaps carnitine or Vitamin B_{12}). The small number unclassified is a testimony to the completeness of our knowledge of elementary biochemistry. Although 18 Ophiostoma mutants had undiscovered needs, none responded to Vitamin A.

Having roughly classified the mutants, the next step is to see whether the same normal gene is altered in two similar mutants. In Neurospora we can cross them. If all the progeny of two "arginineless" mutants are arginineless, it is generally assumed that the same gene is affected in both. This is, however, not necessarily so. Two genes concerned in different steps of the same synthesis are often close together on a chromosome. This means that recombination, which would give a "prototroph," that is to say a mycelium which will grow on the minimal medium, occurs very rarely. In other species crossing is more difficult, or even impossible. Pontecorvo has so far only analysed about 60 of over 600 mutants genetically, and has only located 27 on chromosomes. This is, however, no mean achievement. It is about the number located in domestic poultry in half a century. But it means that, for example, of the five "ornithineless-arginineless" auxotrophs which he obtained, one can only say that at least two are at different loci. Two other methods of getting similar information are as follows. We can grow the two in a mixed culture. If one of them liberates a substance which the other can use but not make, they may be able to live together. In some species, especially the asexual ones, hyphae may fuse to give a "heterokaryon," a mycelium containing two different kinds of nuclei. This may be capable of life on the minimal medium. Hetero-karyons are far from being mere laboratory artefacts. They are common in nature, and many strains used in industry are heterokaryons.

Further steps are the location of genes at definite loci on different chromosomes, and the analysis by various methods of their bio-chemical actions. A classical case is the analysis by Srb and Horowitz (1944) of fifteen arginineless mutants of *N. crassa*. Eight were con-sidered to be duplicates. The other seven gave the results shown in Table 5, along with similar results obtained by Bonner (1946) in *Penicillium notatum*, and by Pontecorvo *et al.* (1952), in *Aspergillus nidulans*. It is clear that in the first two species there is full agreement with the hypothesis (Fig. 1) that arginine is synthesized from orni-thine through citrulline, as it is in some (but perhaps not all) mammalian livers. In arg-1 the step from citrulline to arginine is blocked, in arg-2 and arg-3 that from ornithine to citrulline. There may be two steps, or perhaps two genes are needed to make an enzyme, or one to make an enzyme and another a coenzyme. On the other hand, citrulline is apparently not an intermediate in *A. nidulans*. If it is so we must assume that the mycelial membrane, though permeable to ornithine and arginine, is impermeable to citrulline, which seems very improbable. More remarkably the "ornithineless" and the two "prolineless" mutants seem to show that neither orni-thine nor proline is intermediate in arginine synthesis, even though most of the "arginineless" mutants can utilize either of these substances. The table does *not* prove that proline was one. The mutant 35784 in Penicillium requires proline, and we must suppose that the function lost is the capacity for reversible transformation of

TABLE 5

Species	Mutant	Glutamic acid	Proline	Ornithine	Citrulline	Arginine
Neurospora	arg-8, 9	?	+	+	+	+
crassa	arg-4, 5, 6, 7	?	−	+	+	+
	arg-2, 3	?	−	−	+	+
	arg-1	?	−	−	−	+
Penicillium	24033	+	+	+	+	+
notatum	35784	−	+	−	−	−
	9929	−	+	+	+	+
	6155	−	−	+	+	+
	6572	−	−	±	+	+
	3485	−	−	−	−	+
Aspergillus	one	+	+	+	−	+
nidulans	fourteen	−	+	+	−	+
	five	−	−	+	−	+
	one	−	−	−	−	+
	one	−	−	+	−	−
	two	−	+	−	−	−

proline into an intermediate. In 6572 the synthesis of citrulline from ornithine appears to be difficult.

Table 6 (after Catcheside and others) records all the biochemical mutants of *Neurospora crassa* which had been located on the chromosomes up to about 1948. It reflects to some extent the interests of the workers concerned, and does not include, for example, mutants requiring acetate, nitrite, and sulphanilamide. The list is, however, clearly far from complete. It only includes a few of those which, although requiring some constituents of the complete medium, are inhibited by others. No attempt has been made to find mutants which require such substances as the glucose phosphates, which have disappeared from the complete medium as the result of autolysis, still less those requiring substances to which the hyphal membrane is impermeable. Probably most biochemical mutations do not completely suppress growth on minimal medium.

Before we consider particular cases of amino-acid synthesis, let us begin with an elementary point due to Fincham (1950). A mutant shown to "need" a given amino-acid will often grow on the corresponding α-keto-acid. This has been shown for methionine, valine, leucine, and arginine. Where an α-keto-acid is not available such a mutant will often grow on the corresponding D-amino-acid, since Neurospora possesses a powerful D-amino-acid oxidase. This,

C

TABLE 6

Genetically analysed auxotrophic mutants of Neurospora crassa.

Requirements (always alternative except for valine and isoleucine)	Number of loci
Nitrite, ammonia ..	1
Ammonia ..	1
Glycine, serine	1
α-aminobutyric acid, threonine ..	1
Threonine ..	1
Threonine, isoleucine	1
Homoserine	1
Valine	1
Valine + isoleucine	1
Leucine	2
α-aminoadipic acid, lysine	1
Lysine	3
Proline	1
Proline, ornithine, citrulline, arginine ..	1
Ornithine, citrulline, arginine	4
Citrulline, arginine	2
Arginine ..	2
Histidine ..	1
Phenylalanine	1
Anthranilic acid, indole, tryptophan	3
Indole, tryptophan	2
Tryptophan	1
Cysteic acid, cysteine-sulphinic acid, cysteine	1
Cysteine-sulphinic acid, cysteine	1
Cysteine ..	1
Cysteine, cystathionine, homocysteine, methionine ..	1
Cystathionine, homocysteine, methionine	1
Homocysteine, methionine	1
Methionine	3
	40
Inositol	1*
Choline	2
Pantothenic acid ..	1*
p-aminobenzoic acid	3
Pyridoxine	2*
Tryptophan, nicotinic acid	1
Nicotinic acid	2
Thiazole, thiamine	2
Thiamine ..	4*
	18

* Several "allelomorphs" are known at one or more of these loci. It is quite possible that any or all of these are at closely linked and biochemically co-operating loci.

TABLE 6—*continued*

Requirements (always alternative except for valine and isoleucine)	Number of loci
Hypoxanthine, adenine	5*
Adenine	1*
Cytidine, uridine	4*
	10
Acetate	2
Succinate	2
Sulphonamide	2

* Several "allelomorphs" are known at one or more of these loci. It is quite possible that any or all of these are at closely linked and biochemically co-operating loci.

however, will not attack D-serine, D-lysine, or D-tryptophan. Fincham worked with a mutant 32213 (= 47305) which will grow on any of fifteen amino-acids but on none of the keto-acids or D-amino-acids tested. Growth is particularly good with glutamic and aspartic acids and ornithine, but does not occur with glycine, serine, threonine, lysine and some others. Ammonia tends to accumulate in the medium. This mutant, like the wild type, has at least two transaminases. It apparently lacks some part of the glutamic dehydrogenase system, with which a normal mycelium makes glutamic acid from ammonia and α-ketoglutaric acid.

Lysine is a special case (Mitchell and Houlahan, 1948). Mutant 33393 (lysineless) will grow on lysine, or on L- or DL-α-amino-adipic acid. That is to say, it can attach an amino group to the ϵ carbon atom, perhaps by reducing the amide. But it will not grow on α-keto-adipic acid. Three other lysineless mutants (4544, 15069, and 37101) will not grow on α-amino-adipic acid, nor will any of the lysineless Aspergillus mutants, and it is presumed that three stages in its conversion to lysine are blocked in them. It is surprising that D-α-amino-adipic acid seems to be fully utilized in presence of its L-isomer, while the keto-acid is not used. Windsor (1951) later showed by radioactive labelling that α-amino-adipic acid is converted into lysine, and no other amino-acid, by 33933.

Let us now consider in further detail the synthesis of some amino-acids. A group of at least twelve different mutants will not grow in minimal medium, but require some or all of cysteine, methionine, and threonine. The unexpected appearance of threonine in this

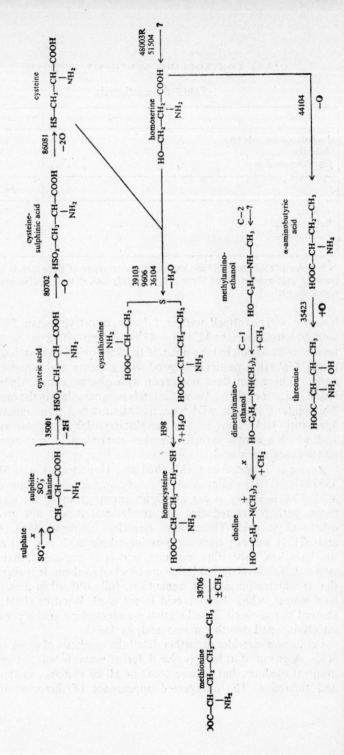

FIG. 1

context is due to the discovery by Teas, Horowitz and Fling (1948) that mutant 51504 needs L- or D-methionine, *and* L-threonine. They later found that it could grow on L-homoserine, or on L-threonine plus D-homoserine or β-hydroxy-L-homoserine. More surprisingly the "homoserineless" mutant 46003-R will grow on canavanine (Teas, 1951). Fig. 1 shows the various relations revealed by their work and that of others.

The number above an arrow is the number of the mutant in which the corresponding step is blocked. The symbols below it represent the chemical change, a reduction, oxidation, hydrolysis or its reverse, or a methylation. It may be remarked that cystine can often (? always) replace cysteine, but homocystine will not replace homocysteine, though DL-homocystine thiolactone will do so. The path from cysteine + homoserine to methionine was studied by Horowitz (1947). H 98, when grown in presence of 25 mg/litre DL-methionine, accumulated a substance, mainly in the mycelium, which supported growth of 36104. The yield was 360 mg. per kilogram wet weight and it was shown to be L-cystathionine, which has three optical isomers. Both D- and L-allocystathionine, each of which has one "looking-glass" carbon atom, had a slight effect in supporting the growth of 39816, in which the block occurs before the cysteine stage: D-cystathionine, which has two "unnatural" asymmetric carbon atoms, was quite ineffective. It will be seen that this rather elaborate process is used to transfer a sulphur atom from the three-carbon chain of cysteine to the four-carbon chain of homoserine. In the rat's liver homocysteine and serine give cystathionine and thence cysteine and homoserine, that is to say two or more metabolic steps occur in the reverse direction.

Many more additions could be made to Fig. 1, mainly as the result of work by various authors summarized by Emerson (1950). In three different mutants the step from homoserine to cystathionine is blocked. Each of them accumulates a substance or substances (presumably other than cysteine and homoserine) which will allow 51504 to grow without methionine or threonine. The cystathionine precursor may be optically inactive at least as regards the α-carbon of homoserine, since it is formed from D-homoserine. Further 9666 accumulates threonine. The methylation of homocysteine is a complex process blocked in no less than ten mutants, whose allelomorphism is under investigation. The methyl probably comes from choline since C-1 and C-2 can grow for a time, but not indefinitely, on methionine alone, and 37603 will grow well on choline or methionine, but not on homocysteine. The source of the methyl groups in choline, which seems to be produced by further methylation of amino-ethanol, is unknown. The evidence for the complexity of the methylation process is as follows. Most mutants, e.g. 86081, 9666 and H 98, can reduce selenite. One of the mutants blocking methylation always reduces selenite, others can only do so if extra methionine is added. Three more can never do so. Finally, p-amino-benzoic acid is somehow involved in methylation, since methionine, but not homocysteine, reduces the p-amino-benzoic-acid requirements of the p-amino-benzoicless mutant, 1633.

It is impossible to describe all the experimental work summarized in Fig. 1. It is, however, notable that L-homoserine has been isolated from cultures of 9606 supplied with threonine and methionine. Presumably the step blocked in H 98 produces serine as well as homocysteine, but we cannot hope to find a mutant in which serine accumulates, for a block to the utilization of serine would prevent normal protein synthesis, and a gene causing it would be an unconditional lethal.

An equally remarkable series of researches is summarized in Fig. 2, though it must be emphasized that it is far from complete. The first observation made was that some mutants could be kept alive either by a protein digest or the B vitamins. Further precision showed a need for tryptophan or nicotinic acid, nicotinamide being equally useful. Other mutants require nicotinic acid but can make tryptophan. Anthranilic acid was detected by its fluorescence and later isolated from a "tryptophanless," 10575. The other intermediates were similarly detected and shown to replace tryptophan or nicotinic acid. 3-hydroxy-kynurenine had been isolated from mutant Drosophila (see Chapter VI). 3416 produces quinolinic acid from tryptophan; and this is clearly not an intermediate, as none of the nicotinamide-requiring mutants can use it. Anthranilic acid is accumulated, though not in large amounts, in some mutants when supplied with kynurenine, but the details of the cycle are far from clear. Isotopic studies show that in mutants where tryptophan synthesis is blocked, all the N atoms of nicotinic acid are derived from the ring N atom of tryptophan.

Nevertheless, Bonner, Yanofsky and Partridge (1952) have shown that the notion of metabolic blocks, while heuristically valuable, is much too simple. 39401 will grow on nicotinic acid alone, and if given nicotinic acid, can then make tryptophan from labelled anthranilic acid. Similar experiments were made with other mutants, combined with 3416, which diverts the precursor of nicotinic acid into quinolinic acid. They were given unlabelled nicotinic acid and

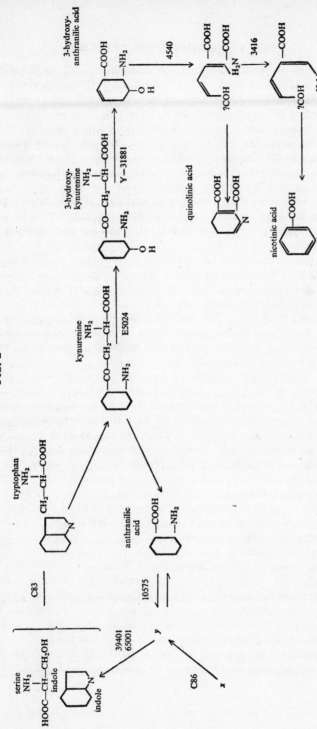

Fig. 2

N^{15}-labelled tryptophan, indole, or anthranilic acid. C-83, 3416* showed a complete block. When fed on labelled tryptophan, both the tryptophan and quinolinic acid isolated from it had 94–99% of the expected N^{15} content, but 75001, 3416 and 7655, 3416* behaved differently. All can normally make tryptophan from indole or anthranilic acid, but not from minimal medium. Under various conditions 16–80% of the tryptophan and 29–100% of the quinolinic acid was derived from the labelled source. Various possibilities such as reversion and N exchange were ruled out.

It was concluded that a number of mutants, though they cannot grow on minimal medium without a substance, can yet make this substance when growing. The authors describe this phenomenon as "leakage."

This phenomenon must be considered in connection with Wagner's (1949) finding that although certain mutants need pantothenic acid, and cannot synthesize it from pantoyl lactone and β-alanine, an enzyme system which carries out this synthesis can, nevertheless, be extracted from them. This decisively disproves the one-gene-one-enzyme hypothesis as being universally valid in its original form. There are many possible reasons for blockage in a mutant, one being the presence of an inhibitor.

Once again, other organisms have different synthetic paths. Pontecorvo, et al. (1952), obtained nine mutants in *Aspergillus nidulans* which will grow on nicotinic acid, or (unlike Neurospora mutants) on quinolinic acid. Four of these also grow on anthranilic acid, indole, tryptophan, kynurenine, 3-hydroxy-kynurenine, or 3-hydroxy-anthranilic acid, though nic-3 requires very large amounts of tryptophan or anthranilic acid. The other five, however, which will grow on 3-hydroxy-anthranilic acid, or on very large amounts of anthranilic, will not grow at all on indole, tryptophan or kynurenine. This suggests the presence of a not very efficient "tryptophan by-pass," allowing the direct oxidation of anthranilic acid, in place of the very round-about route of Fig. 2.

Similar investigations into the origin of valine and isoleucine (Bonner, 1946b; Adelberg, Bonner and Tatum, 1951; Tatum and Adelberg, 1951) yielded the following results. 16117 needs valine *and* isoleucine for growth. 33051 grows at about half the normal rate on valine, while isoleucine brings the rate up to normal. In each case growth is best when the two acids are present in about equimolar concentrations, and it became clear that the requirement of relatively large amounts of valine by 16117 was due to the

* i.e. the double mutant produced by crossing these two mutants.

accumulation of an isoleucine precursor which inhibited valine synthesis. This turned out to be α-β-dihydroxy-β-ethylbutyric acid. The corresponding methyl compound is a valine precursor (Fig. 3).

FIG. 3

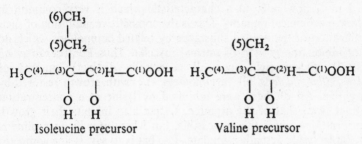

Isoleucine precursor   Valine precursor

When the carbon source was C-labelled acetate it was found that carbon 5 is mainly derived from the methyl group of the acetate, which also contributes to carbons 1 or 2 and 4, but not to 3. Similarly the carboxyl group contributes to 6, to 1 and 2, and to some extent to 3, but not to 3 or 5. Umbarger and Adelberg (1951) have made it highly probable that these acids are converted to the corresponding keto-acids by the normal fungus. This interesting molecular rearrangement is blocked in 16117. Perhaps it lacks an isomerase. Wright (1951) found that a mutant requiring serine or glycine grew satisfactorily on glycollic or glyoxylic acid.

I must pass over a large amount of work on purine and pyrimidine syntheses, merely noting a few facts. Adenine-requiring mutants in this and other species often accumulate pigment, and are thus identified without special methods. Thus adenineless 35203 accumulates a purple pigment, which is probably fairly close to adenine, as three other adenineless mutants, when combined with 35203, suppress its formation (Mitchell and Houlahan, 1946). Two points come out clearly from the work on pyrimidineless mutants. Orotic acid (4-carboxy-uracil) can be a substitute for uracil in some (Lorenz and Pierce, 1944) and accumulates in another (Mitchell, Houlahan and Nyc, 1948), reaching a concentration of 1·3 gm/litre, which is almost saturated, in the culture medium. It is not necessarily a normal intermediate. However, Mitchelson, Drell and Mitchell (1951) isolated orotidine, orotic acid riboside, from 36001 (pyrimidineless) in a yield of nearly 1% of its dry weight. As a result of this work it has been shown to play a part in mammalian pyrimidine metabolism.

Mitchell and Houlahan (1947) find that oxaloacetic acid and amino-fumaric diamide will support a rather slow growth in some of these mutants. Secondly Houlahan and Mitchell (1948b) find that several lysineless mutants accumulate pyrimidines. The significance of this is not clear.

I must now refer to a characteristic which is very common in these biochemical mutants. This is the competitive inhibition of their utilization of the needed substance by related compounds which do not inhibit the growth of normal mycelia. Thus Pontecorvo et al. (1952) studied eight (not all necessarily distinct) mutants of *Aspergillus nidulans*, all "arginineless," i.e. with growth restored by arginine. All of them were inhibited by lysine at a concentration about twice that of the arginine. Lysine also inhibits their growth on ornithine where this is possible, but where growth on proline is possible, lysine actually stimulates it. That is to say, lysine competes with arginine or ornithine supplied from outside, but not with arginine formed by the normal synthetic process. Perhaps the uptake of amino-acids by a hypha is a process as complicated as their re-absorption by the human kidney (cf. Chapter VI) and will have to be investigated on similar lines. Competition may, of course, also occur for intracellular enzymes, but it is clear that the genetic blocking of a reaction may well be due to the accumulation of an intermediate.

A very remarkable case was investigated by Emerson (1947) and Zalokar (1948). Several sulphanilamide-resistant forms were obtained by selection. One (*sfo*) was found to need sulphanilamide (about 10^{-4} M) at high temperatures. The normal mould is inhibited in minimal medium $+ 0 \cdot 5$ M sulphanilamide, and grows slowly if even 10^{-6} M p-amino-benzoic acid is added. Another mutant (*pab*) needs p-amino-benzoic acid.

On combining the two we get the situation shown in Fig. 4 where the growth rate in mm. per hour is plotted against concentration of p-amino-benzoic acid. *pab,sfo* is poisoned by too much of this substance. Later Emerson (1950) discovered that methionine and threonine are also involved. Double mutants of the sulphanilamide-requiring strain and those with blocks to homocysteine synthesis grow if a little methionine is added. If more than a little is added they require sulphanilamide. The sulphanilamide-requiring strain will also grow when threonine is added. It appears that in the sulphanilamide-requiring strain an aberrant reaction is taking place which uses up homo-cysteine and threonine, and is catalysed by p-amino-benzoic acid. The details are complicated, and until the nature of the reaction catalysed by p-amino-benzoic acid is known, the matter will not be cleared up.

FIG. 4

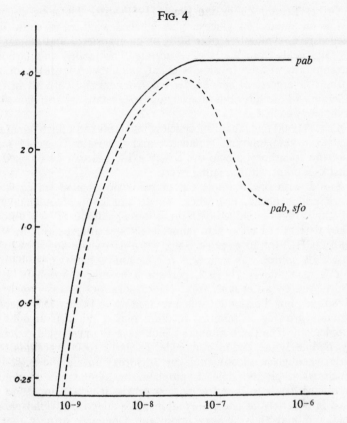

Among non-nitrogenous metabolites the most interesting work is perhaps that on "acetateless" mutants, of which there are at least three genetically different ones. All of them require acetate, ethanol, or perhaps other simple substances, if glucose is the sole carbon source. They grow slowly on glycerol as sole carbon source, but even a little glucose prevents such growth. It seems that some product of the normal metabolism of glucose inhibits the utilization of glycerol for acetate formation. Lein and Lein (1952) worked with a suppressor of "acetateless," that is to say a mutant which enables all three acetateless mutants to grow in presence of glucose, though slowly. In two cases the growth was at just the same rate as on glycerol only. It is suggested that the suppressor blocks the production from glucose of the substance which prevents the utilization of glycerol.

Ottke, Tatum, Zubin and Bloch (1951) used this same mutant, living on unlabelled glucose plus labelled acetate, to show that Neurospora synthesizes over 90% of its ergosterol and almost all its fatty acids from the labelled acetate. The methyl and carboxyl carbons are utilized in almost equal amounts. About 1% of the carbon in ergosterol can be derived from methyl carbons in iso-valerate, whose previous conversion to acetate is not, however, completely excluded.

Lewis (1948) finds that "succinicless" mutants can utilize fumarate, malate, α-ketoglutarate, glutamate, and aspartate. It would seem that the tricarboxylic acid cycle may exist, but can be blocked at least one point without lethal effect.

I end with one example out of many possible where genetical work points ahead, just where we do not know. Houlahan and Mitchell (1948) examined trichloracetic acid extracts of Neurospora. They determined phosphate immediately and after heating at 100° with 2N HCl for 10 minutes. Some extra phosphate appeared in all cases. Its source was mainly a polymetaphosphate whose barium salt is insoluble in 1N HCl, perhaps a hexametaphosphate. It is hydrolysed by an enzyme from Neurospora. Some was present in all strains, but the amount was increased up to twenty-fold in some mutants growing in minimal medium plus a minimal amount of supplement. The three mutants which gave the best yield required pyrimidine, lysine, and nicotinamide. The latter (65001) accumulated little when given nicotinamide or 3-hydroxy-anthranilic acid, but much when given indole, tryptophan, or kynurenine. A similar substance has been found in normal yeasts. It would appear to be used in a variety of phosphorylations, like adenosine-triphosphoric acid, and may thus be very important. One may surmise that it plays a less important but perhaps essential part in higher organisms.

Apart from "leakage," a good many examples of partial metabolic blocks have been recorded. Thus Houlahan and Mitchell (1947) described three allelomorphic mutants (in which the same normal gene, or perhaps two or three very closely linked genes, has been altered). Their behaviour is summarized in Table 7.

Thus pyr-3^b grows normally on minimal medium at 25° but is lethal at 35° C. This may be due to a different temperature coefficient of a catalysis, to the more rapid heat inactivation of an enzyme, or even to a need for CO_2 in the medium (Borek and Waelsch, 1951). It is clear that genes with quantitative effects of this kind are more like those studied in other organisms than are the majority of those so far described in Neurospora.

TABLE 7

Amounts of hydrolysed nucleic acid in gm/litre needed for half maximal growth

Mutant	Nucleotide need	
	25° C	35° C
37301 = pyr-3[a]	3·3	3·15
67602 = pyr-3[c]	0·38	2·3
37813 = pyr-3[b]	0	2·4

A few general remarks on this work may be made. To a "classical" biochemist (which means, in fact, one who has accepted the point of view of Hopkins) this work must seem incomplete because in rather few cases have the enzymes concerned been even approximately isolated, and compared with yeast or mammalian muscle the systems concerned are ill understood. In particular it is likely that many phosphoric esters remain to be discovered. As against this, wholly new fields of intermediary metabolism have been opened up. It is, moreover, possible that more is known than has been published. Some of the workers concerned are now paid by the Atomic Energy Commission, and such an affiliation at best imposes a delay on publication, at worst holds it up indefinitely.

It is clear that we must abandon the hypothesis that every genetically determined block is always due to a failure to produce the catalyst concerned in the blocked process. A block can be due to inhibition by a metabolic product often chemically related to the substance which is not utilized, and probably to other causes. This does not, however, disprove the hypothesis that enzymes are direct gene products. The activity of enzyme α on substrate A may be blocked because enzyme β is abnormally active, producing an inhibitor B, or because enzyme γ, which normally converts B into something else, is absent, or abnormally inactive, because the permeability of a membrane has been altered, and so on. It is still possible that α is a primary gene product. Similarly in physiology, the fact that the testes of an animal do not produce testosterone in adequate amounts if the anterior pituitary, or even the eyes, are not performing their normal functions, in no way disproves the hypothesis that testosterone is formed by the testes. The analogy with diabetes mellitus (p. 76) is perhaps even more instructive.

CHAPTER IV

Biochemical Genetics of Yeasts, Bacteria, and Viruses

Yeasts are, of course, a specialized and morphologically degenerate group of fungi, mostly, perhaps, ascomycetes.

The cytology is very difficult. It is generally thought that most yeast cells (particularly those of the common baker's and brewer's yeasts, *Saccharomyces cerevisiae*) are diploid. They can often be induced to give rise to four-spored asci. The spores may conjugate at once on germination, or propagate themselves for some time as haploids. There are a good many inherited biochemical characters, but their genetics are a matter of controversy (cf. Catcheside, *l.c.*). Winge, in Denmark, obtains results showing fairly clear Mendelian segregation. Lindegren and Spiegelman in America describe very irregular segregation, and transmission of acquired ability to ferment melibiose (cf. Chapter VII) for a thousand cell generations. Until this controversy is settled it is premature to draw far-reaching conclusions from the genetical data. It seems likely that some of the irregular segregation observed may be explained by polyploidy. Winge and Roberts (1948), who obtained good Mendelian segregations, attribute the results of others to the presence of several genes with like effects, and to overlap of generations. Their most recent work (Winge and Roberts, 1952) deals with the following genes:

R_1, R_2, R_3. Each produces a β-fructofuranosidase, permitting the fermentation of sucrose and raffinose, adaptation requiring 5 hours or less.

M_1 produces an α-glucopyranosidase, and can ferment maltose or sucrose, but only after one or more days.

M_2 produces a specific maltase which does not allow the fermentation of sucrose, even after fourteen days' training in 1% glucose + 1% sucrose.

M_3 and M_4 produce a maltase of some kind, but have not yet been obtained without any of the other genes mentioned, so the specificity of the enzymes produced by them is not clear.

M_1 and R_1 are very closely linked, with about 1% recombination, which gave m_1r_1 cells which could not ferment sucrose.

It is, however, to be noted that among 241 asci from which 964 spores were isolated and followed up, the authors find it necessary to postulate no less than three mutations affecting the rather few genes with which they were working. Rates of this order are pretty well unknown elsewhere except for the "multimutating" genes which cause flaking in flowers. It may therefore be that their interpretation is not final.

Biochemical mutants of the type described in the last chapter are known, and here yeast offers one considerable technical advantage. If two biochemical mutants are known, we can plate out a mixture of them on a minimal medium. Since abilities to make a substance or to utilize one are usually dominant, the surviving prototrophic cells are generally diploids with the normal dominant genes from both strains. Single cell cultures of these will segregate out forms with double biochemical deficiencies as haploids or double recessives.

In view of our extensive knowledge of the dynamical biochemistry of yeast, a really satisfactory technique for the genetical treatment of its biochemical mutants will be of the greatest importance. The work of Subramaniam (1945 and later) and his colleagues may point the way to important advances.

The violence (whether justifiable posterity may decide) of the language used regarding yeast genetics can only be paralleled in connection with the differences of opinion between Soviet workers and those of most other countries on general genetics. "—— and his colleagues have come to presumptuous conclusions as a result of their superficial investigations" is a typical example. No one who has not worked on yeast genetics can presume to judge in this matter. We can only be glad that it is not yet mixed up with politics!

Bacterial genetics are difficult. Abnormal races are obtained either by plating out individuals, usually after treatment which induces gene mutations in higher organisms, or by selection for resistance to a drug or a bacteriophage. In the latter case it is extremely hard to distinguish between adaptation and selection. Only in a very few strains is sexual reproduction known. In other cases we can say that two "mutants" with the same biochemical requirement (e.g. pyrimidine) are different if they grow together, in a mixed culture, each producing a diffusible substance which supplements the other's needs; but we cannot state that the same gene has mutated if they do not do so. Table 8 (after Catcheside 1951 and Lederberg 1948) is a list of some known mutants in *Escherichia coli*. Some at least

TABLE 8

Some mutants of Escherichia coli

Requiring sulphite Requiring sulphide	Requiring methionine
Requiring pantothenic acid Requiring p-aminobenzoic acid Requiring pyridoxin Requiring nicotinamide Requiring biotin Requiring thiamine	Requiring purines Requiring pyrimidines
	Unable to ferment maltose Unable to ferment lactose
Requiring threonine Requiring glutamic acid Requiring glutamine Requiring leucine Requiring isoleucine Requiring lysine Requiring proline Requiring arginine Requiring phenylalanine Requiring tyrosine Requiring tryptophan Requiring cystine Requiring homocysteine	Resistant to lithium chloride Resistant to azide Resistant to dichloracetate Resistant to sulphonamide Resistant to radiations and to mustard gas Resistant to various strains of phage

of the phage-resistant mutants also come under "amino-acidless" auxotrophs, as they require tryptophan in their medium. Similarly chloracetate-resistant forms do not form CO_2 from sugars, apparently lacking carboxylase. The fact that the same mutation confers resistance both to chemical and physical mutagens strongly supports the view (see Chapter VIII) that the action of radiations is fundamentally biochemical.

Multiple mutants are known. Thus Lederberg (1948) obtained a threonineless form by X-radiation. Further X-radiation gave leucineless and thiamineless; ultraviolet radiation removed the capacity to ferment lactic acid; and selective killing added resistance to a phage strain. Reversion to normal occurs by mutation, but only of one gene at a time. When, however, two multiple mutant auxotrophic stocks of a particular strain, K12, of *E. coli*, which between them contain a set of normal genes, are mixed, small numbers of prototrophs appear. Lederberg has made it reasonably certain that this occurs as a result of an interaction of bacteria in pairs (never in triads) and that the genes show linkage as if they were arranged on a single chromosome. Lederberg (1949) has further obtained rather unstable diploid stocks in which the normal characteristics are dominant. Lederberg's findings have been fully confirmed, and there can be no doubt of the importance of his discovery, but his interpretation of them as analogous to the sexual process in higher organisms is open to question. Hayes (1952a, 1952b) worked with two K12 strains, 58–161 which requires biotin and methionine, and W667, which requires thiamine, threonine, and leucine. They give prototrophic "recombinants" under Lederberg's conditions. If W667 has previously been treated with streptomycin or ultraviolet radiation in doses sufficient to "kill" it, that is to say to prevent it permanently from multiplying, no recombinants are produced; but such previous treatment of 58–161 does not stop the formation of recombinants, and ultraviolet radiation can even increase it up to twenty-five times. He concludes that 58–161 acts as a donor of nuclear material even when its cytoplasm has been so damaged as to prevent reproduction. W667 is a receptor (he avoids the words male and female) and the integrity of its cytoplasm is essential.

But other unit characters in bacteria are inherited in a different way, perhaps first demonstrated by Wollman and Wollman (1925). Pneumococcus can be classified into over fifty serological types on the basis of their capsular polysaccharides, which are antigens of very different compositions, e.g. some contain amino sugar residues, others do not. When grown on media not containing vertebrate sera, they "degenerate," and form rough colonies instead of the normal smooth ones. The capsular polysaccharides are lost along with the virulence, but both can be regained in a suitable medium. When, however, a smooth form, derived, say, from rough Type II, is grown in suitable circumstances in presence of a cell-free extract of Type III, it develops into a rough Type III. Avery, Macleod and McCarty (1944) purified the "transforming principle," and showed that it is a desoxyribonucleic acid, stable to proteases, amylases and ribonuclease, but destroyed by desoxyribonuclease. Hotchkiss (1949) describes the further purification. His best fractions had half the maximum activity at a concentration of 7×10^{-8}, or [since the molecular weight is of the order of 6×10^6, according to the results of Tuke, Drew and Pollard (1952) with deuteron bombardment] at about 10^{-11} molar. Since there is no reason to suppose that even 1% of this nucleic acid has the highly specific function of the transforming principle, the real concentration may be much less. The hydrolysate contains no uracil, but perhaps some 5-methyl-cytosine.

D

Taylor (1949) has carried the matter further. For transformation the smooth bacteria must be held for about five hours with an agglutinating factor such as an antiserum, and another protein factor such as crystalline serum albumin. It is suggested that their function is to retard nucleic acid synthesis. Then 5 minutes' incubation with the transforming principle suffices. In 30 minutes about one Pneumococcus in 200 is transformed. Taylor has further worked with "extreme roughs" of Type III, and intermediates. She has shown that several "races" producing different amounts of what is at least antigenically the same polysaccharide produce qualitatively different transforming principles. Transforming principles will convert a rough type into a smooth type producing Type II or Type VI capsular polysaccharide. What is much more remarkable, she has obtained crossing-over of transforming principles. That is to say, by "infecting" Pneumococci with principles causing them to perform processes A and B separately, she has obtained a principle which causes them to perform both A and B, the two effects being now inseparable, or very nearly so. For a summary of work on these and other bacteria, see Boivin, Vendrely and Tulasne (1949). Boivin, Vendrely and Le Hoult (1945) were able to transfer the capacity for making saccharase from one strain of *E. coli* to another by a similar technique. Other workers have claimed similar transfers even between species. Thus Jermoljeva and Bujanowska (1927) had produced luminous forms of *Vibrio cholerae* by growing them with *Vibrio phosphorescens*. These claims have become quite plausible.

Let us be clear what has happened. A Pneumococcus takes up one or more molecules of nucleic acid of a certain pattern from solution. As a result it makes more of this particular type of nucleic acid, as do its descendants; and it also makes a particular kind of polysaccharide. Since the transforming principle is not destroyed by amylase, it is unlikely that the nucleic acid contains the polysaccharide as a prosthetic group. When we further consider that chromosomes, at some stages in their "life" cycle, consist of desoxyribose-nucleic acid and very simple proteins, it seems reasonable to suppose that the transforming principle is not unlike a gene detached from its chromosome.

There may be yet a third type of reproductive "mechanism" in bacteria. Many types of bacteria are destroyed by phage, which multiplies 100–300 times in the process. A very few resistant mutants escape, and apparently do not harbour phage. There are, however, lysogenic strains of bacteria which harbour phage, but only occasionally liberate it, in which case it can attack other bacteria.

In some cases phage is only liberated in very special circumstances. That is to say, the rate of reproduction of phage is almost exactly equal to that of the bacteria. Nevertheless in exceptional circumstances phage can pass from one bacterium to another. Here then is another case of transfer. A phage particle has a molecular weight of the order of 10^8 or 10^9, which is intermediate between that of a nucleic acid molecule and that of a chromosome. Since this paragraph was written Hayes (1952b) calls attention to the fact that Weigle and Delbrück (1951) have shown that Lederberg's K12 strain harbours a virus liberated by ultraviolet radiation, and discusses the possibility that the "genes" transferred in Lederberg's experiments are carried by, or are part of, this virus, or phage. This is, of course, a return to older ideas that phage was part of the life cycle of bacteria. Until these questions are cleared up it is perhaps premature to homologize bacterial genes too closely with those of larger organisms.

Phage has its own genetics. Mutations occur, and as the result of a mixed infection, phage particles are formed combining some of the characters of both their "parents." Some of the mutant forms differ antigenically. Others require "activation" before they will attack a bacillus. Delbrück (1949) described races of T4 with different needs. One stock has no such needs. The normal type requires about 10^{-5} M L-tryptophan, or other substances in much larger concentrations. Another mutant requires tryptophan and Ca^{++}. Some of the tryptophan-requiring stocks are inhibited by small quantities of indole, others are not. Estimates of the number of genes vary from about 20 to over 100. If this means that a phage contains only some fifty molecular species of desoxyribonucleic acid their separation becomes a task which would certainly be formidable, but incomparably easier than the isolation of one of 10,000 or so genes from a metazoan chromosome, supposing each gene to be a separate molecular species. It is possible that the first genes to be isolated will be genes from bacteriophage. On the other hand, the purification of a transforming principle may be simpler. But it is perhaps in these simple organisms that the material basis of inheritance will first be specifiable in chemical terms.

Comparatively little work has been done in using series of mutants to detect metabolic pathways in bacteria, though doubtless a careful search of the literature would permit the compilation of relevant results. I therefore take two examples to illustrate the lines on which such work is developing. Plough, Miller and Berry (1951) worked on the needs of different mutants of *Salmonella typhimurium*.

They report the following alternative needs:

Cysteine ⎱ cysteine⎱ proline ⎱ tyrosine ⎱
methionine⎰ serine ⎰ glutamic acid⎰ phenylalanine⎰
tyrosine ⎱ adenine⎱
tryptophan⎰ guanine⎰

and as regards sulphur metabolism, the needs shown in Table 9. The normal organism can obtain its sulphur from Na_2SO_4. None of the mutants listed in the table can do so.

TABLE 9

Some auxotrophic mutants of S. typhi murium

Mutant	Na₂S	DL-cysteine	L-cystathionine	DL-homo-cysteine	DL-methionine ---
A141	+	+	+	+	+
B170	+	+	+	+	−
C2031	−	+	+	+	+
D	−	+	+	+	−
E	−	−	+	+	+
F	−	−	−	+	+

It would seem that the metabolic pathway from cysteine to methionine can be traversed in both directions, whereas in rats it appears to be a "one-way street" from methionine to cysteine, in Neurospora from cysteine to methionine. Again Davis (1952) has made it highly probable, from a study of mutants, that *Escherichia coli* forms lysine from $\alpha-\epsilon$-diaminopimelic acid, and not from α-amino-adipic acid. As, however, there is no technique for combining different mutants, conclusions must be much more tentative than in the case of Neurospora; and the history of Neurospora biochemical genetics shows how often mistaken conclusions have been drawn from data which could later be revised by the combination of genetical and biochemical techniques. Except in the rare cases where crossing is possible, this cannot be done with bacteria. Moreover, such work as that of Peacocke and Hinshelwood (1948) shows that some of the effects of ultraviolet radiation are readily reparable by transfer to a suitable medium under conditions which make an explanation by back mutation and selection extremely improbable.

There is no reason to expect *a priori* that the general principles of genetics should hold for bacteria. If some of them do so, that is very satisfying, but it seems equally unwise to argue, except in the most tentative way, from bacterial mutations to mutations in other organisms, or from non-Mendelian behaviour in bacteria against Mendelian behaviour in other organisms.

CHAPTER V

Biochemical Genetics of Higher Plants

Numerous colour varieties of a great many cultivated plants are in existence, and their genetics have been investigated. Often the differences are confined to the flowers, and flower colour has been more intensively studied than that of other organs. However, the stems and leaves generally contain the same anthocyanins as the flowers, though in smaller amounts, and this may be of economic importance, as in onions, where Rieman (1931) found that coloured varieties are resistant to the fungus *Colletotrichum circinans*, apparently because of their protocatechuic acid content. Protocatechuic acid can be derived from cyanidin and quercetin with strong alkalis, and may be their metabolic precursor.

This chapter is a somewhat sad one for me. In 1932 I left the Department of Biochemistry at Cambridge, with a promise that I should be given facilities for the study of biochemical genetics at the John Innes Horticultural Institution. I had hoped, in particular, first to investigate the enzymes concerned in pigment production, and later those concerned in carbohydrate metabolism. For various reasons this promise was not kept, and I found that I was cut off from biochemical research. No one has, in fact, attacked the problems in question, and it was left to Beadle's school to do similar work on simpler organisms.

Flower pigments are almost all of two types. Some flowers have plastid pigments, yellow ether-soluble carotenoids and often a little chlorophyll. The plastids may be absent, as in the rose, present in a central "eye," as in the primrose, or present throughout the petal, as in many Cruciferae. All flowers also possess water-soluble pigments of two related types. The anthocyanins absorb in various parts of the visible spectrum, and vary in colour from red through purple to blue. The anthoxanthins, which may be flavonols, flavones, or chalkones (see Fig. 5) absorb in the violet or near ultraviolet, and are yellow or white. However, all of them are coloured to bees, or

FIG. 5

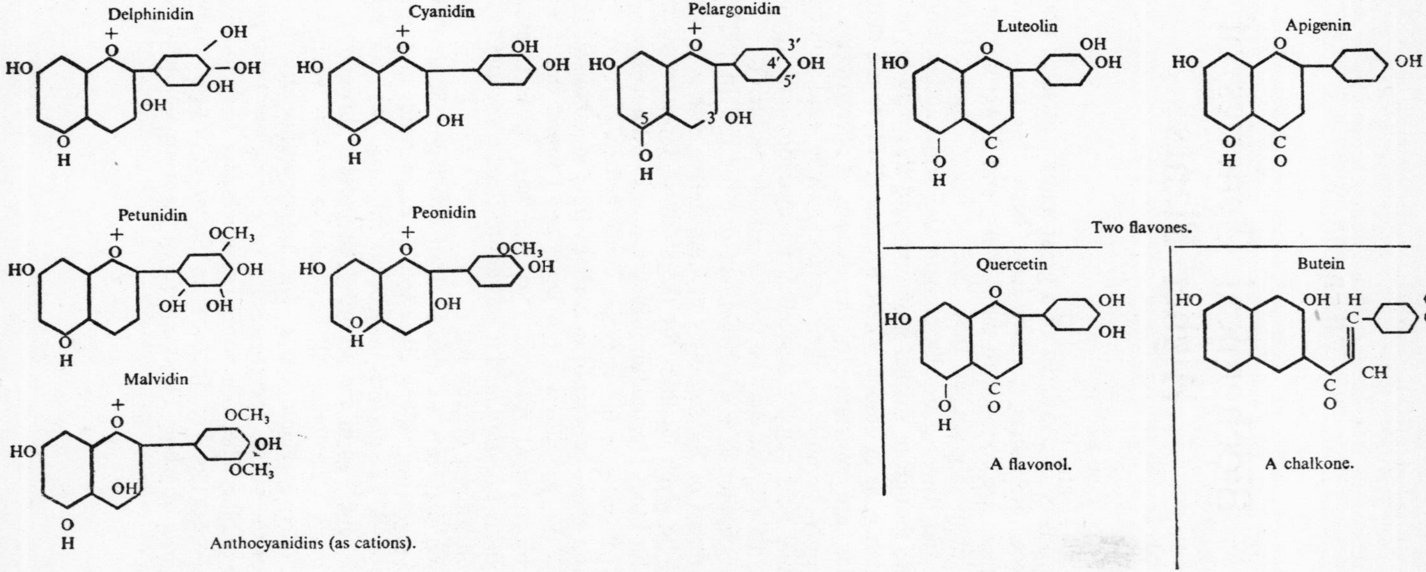
Delphinidin
Cyanidin
Pelargonidin
Petunidin
Peonidin
Malvidin
Luteolin
Apigenin
Quercetin
Butein
HO
OH
OCH₃
3′
4′
5′
5
3

Anthocyanidins (as cations).

Two flavones.

A flavonol.

A chalkone.

more accurately, the bees react differently to an object coloured by a "white" anthoxanthin which absorbs in the near ultraviolet than to an object such as white paper which does not do so. The production of anthocyanins and anthoxanthins is controlled by different genes. Each class of gene may also have structural effects. Thus a recessive gene for large "eye" in *Primula sinensis* gives crimped leaves and petals, one for uniformity of petal colour gives "hooded" standards (petals) in *Lathyrus odoratus*. To get a very dark flower such as the brown wallflower (*Cheiranthus cheiri*) both types of pigment can be used, so that light is absorbed over most of the visible spectrum. Very little is, however, known as to the biochemical genetics of plastid pigments.

The anthocyanins always, and the anthoxanthins usually, exist as glycosides. Fig. 5 gives the constitution of the aglucone residues. The sugars, which may be monoses or bioses, are attached in the 3 or both the 3 and 5 positions. Both types of pigments are indicators. The anthoxanthins become yellow or yellower in alkaline solution, the anthocyanins are red at pH 2–5, often blue at 7–10, and may be purple or colourless in between. However, pelargonidin derivatives do not turn blue. Various colourless organic co-pigments also affect their colours. At a pH round 5 the more hydroxyls are present, either on the anthocyanidin or (though this is much less important) on the sugars, the bluer is the colour. Salmon-pink flowers usually contain pelargonidin derivatives, the most vivid blues delphinidin derivatives. They are present in large amounts, up to 10% or more of the petal dry weight, and their capacity for crystallization makes them far easier to study than most animal pigments.

Flowers of very different colours may contain the same anthocyanin. If so an anthocyanin solution at the pH of the cell sap of the wild plant is usually red, the wild type flower is usually purple, redness being due to a recessive gene, and blueness to a different recessive. At an early stage in her work Scott-Moncrieff (1939) needed great tact to collaborate simultaneously with Sir Robert Robinson and myself. He maintained that blueness was due to organic substances, I was firm that it was due to higher pH. Both turned out to be right. The sap of blue or purple flowers always contains a co-pigment, usually a colourless anthoxanthin, which forms a labile purple compound with anthocyanin. This compound is reversibly dissociated by boiling, or the anthoxanthin can be extracted with ethyl acetate. In red flowers a recessive gene blocks the synthesis of anthoxanthin, and usually leads to an increased production of anthocyanin from their common precursor. In blues the pH of the petal sap, though not that of the leaves or stems, is increased by about 0·6. Thus, using a glass electrode, Scott-Moncrieff found a pH of about 5·3 in purple and red *Primula sinensis*, and of 6·0 in blues, which is the same as that in leaves and stems. The blue or alkaline condition is recessive. Lawrence's (1950) statement to the contrary is incorrect. The alkaline red form is usually a rather dirty purple, and seldom grown commercially.

In white or yellow flowers there is no anthocyanin. This is usually due to a recessive gene blocking synthesis, sometimes to a dominant inhibitor. In most white forms anthoxanthin synthesis is not blocked, on the contrary more than usual is formed. In a few recessive whites (e.g. in *Antirrhinum majus* and *Pharbitis nil*) both anthocyanin and anthoxanthin formation are blocked. Such plants are generally rather feeble. Similarly in the reds where anthoxanthin synthesis is blocked there is usually more anthocyanin than in the purples, where both types of compound are found. Genes are frequently found which regulate the amount of these compounds without suppressing their formation.

Some of the colour differences between domestic varieties are due to differences in oxidation in the 3' and 5' positions, others, generally smaller, to changes in the sugars attached to the main molecule, or to methylation of the hydroxyls. The more oxidized forms are usually, if not always, dominant over the less oxidized, the methylated at least sometimes over the demethylated. Less is known about the genetics of the sugar residues. In Streptocarpus Lawrence (1950) found that the gene *D* generally substitutes a 3-, 5-dihexoside for a 3-bioside (hexose-pentoside), but his results suggest that the second hexose cannot be attached to a pelargonidin residue, so a plant with *D* and the two recessive genes for pelargonidin has a pelargonidin 3-hexoside.

Since both anthocyanins and anthoxanthins can be oxidized in the 3' position by dominant genes, it might be supposed that the same gene would be responsible for both. This is not so in *Antirrhinum majus*, where one dominant gene substitutes cyanidin for pelargonidin, another substitutes the yellow luteolin for the ivory apigenin. In *Primula sinensis* the *kk* (pelargonidin) plants are certainly more liable to fungal attacks and probably weaker in other ways than those containing cyanidin, which is hard to understand if their metabolism is the same except as regards this one molecule.

The biochemical genetics of flower colour is best known in the

sweet pea *Lathyrus odoratus* (Beale *et al.*, 1939). The wild type has
purple flowers, the two lateral petals being lighter and bluer than
the others. Most horticultural varieties are homozygous for a
recessive gene *dw*, and the petals have a more uniform deep colour.
The anthocyanin is mainly malvidin 3 : 5-monoside, the anthoxanthin quercetin, which is colourless but a co-pigment. Smaller
amounts of other related substances are found. The recessive genes
in cultivated forms are as follows:

1. Completely blocking anthocyanin formation *c*, *r*, partially
blocking it, *co*, *p*. The latter gives picotee flowers with little anthocyanin except on the petal borders.

2. Completely blocking anthoxanthin formation, *m*, *k*, partially
blocking it, *h* (and *Dw*), partially blocking it in *co co* plants, *br*.

3. Substituting peonidin for pelargonidin (one methoxyl) *e*,
substituting pelargonidin for peonidin or malvidin, *sm*.

4. Raising petal pH from 5·34 to 5·93 (averages), *d*.

Although no genes blocking synthesis of both anthocyanins and
anthoxanthins are known in this species, the action of these genes
clearly shows that they have a common source. *mm* and *kk* (maroon)
and *mm ee* and *kk ee* (red) flowers have more anthocyanin than the
corresponding co-pigmented types, *co co* and *pp* flowers contain
abnormally large amounts of co-pigment.

There are also unanalysed but hereditary differences in methylation, and some varieties have a considerable amount of a
3-glycoside.

Every plant so far investigated has a slightly different flower
colour genetics. An excellent summary is given by Beale (1941).
Where the wild type is red, anthoxanthin may be absent, as in the
common poppy *Papaver rhoeas* (where it is only found in the dark
basal petal spot). Here the presence of anthoxanthin is recessive to
its absence. While the complete replacement of more oxidized forms
by pelargonidin is always recessive (as if an oxidation were blocked),
one dominant gene in *Primula sinensis* and two in *Papaver rhoeas*
cause formation of pelargonidin along with more oxidized forms.
Fuller details and references are given by Scott-Moncrieff (1939),
Lawrence and Price (1940) and Haldane (1941). As I devoted
27 pages of that book to the genetics of anthocyanins, I deal with
the question in a more summary manner here, but one point may
be noted. A number of genes, usually recessive, suppress anthocyanin formation locally. Thus in *Pisum sativum* the wild type has

anthocyanin in the flowers, the axillae, the pods, and the seed coats. The white-flowered types are due to a recessive gene which blocks anthocyanin formation throughout the plant. Other, different, recessives block it locally in the axillae, pods, and seed coats. Similarly in *Primula sinensis* a dominant gene suppresses anthocyanin formation in the petals. A recessive greatly increases it in the stems and leaves. Most of the other genes affect it throughout the plant. Thus gene changes can produce local chemical differentiation. I know, however, of no case of a gene which alters the chemical nature of the anthocyanin in one part, but not another, of a plant, though they may exist.

As very little research has been done in this field in the last twelve years, it may be worth setting out some of the problems on which I had hoped to carry out or direct research.

1. A search for enzymes responsible for biochemical differences, e.g. a pelargonidin oxidase, and for inhibitors of enzymes. Thus one would look for the absence of an enzyme in a recessive white, for the presence of an inhibitor in a dominant white. Until such work has been done, it is perhaps a mistake to write, as Lawrence (1950) does, "of the conversion of one anthocyanin (malvidin dimonoside) into another (pelargonidin dimonoside) by a single dominant gene." There is not the faintest evidence that the malvidin derivative is first produced and then demethoxylated. If such an event occurs it may occur to the anthocyanin, the anthocyanidin, or a precursor.

2. A full investigation of the sugars of anthocyanins and anthoxanthins. Are they correlated with other glycosides, or with carbohydrate stores in the same plant?

3. Further work on methylation, and an attempt to link it up with the metabolism of methionine or betaines.

4. Investigation of the origin of pH differences (with simultaneous work on the same question in fruits, where it is of economic importance).

5. Attempts to alter flower colour by injecting (*a*) possible selective enzyme inhibitors, and (*b*) possible missing metabolites.

6. These would lead up to an attempt to give an account of anthocyanin formation as full as is that of nicotinamide formation in Neurospora.

7. Once the nature of the chemical process controlled by genes was known, an attempt to explain their morphological effects where these exist.

8. A thorough investigation of gene controlled chemical differentiation.

9. The introduction of a uniform nomenclature for genes controlling similar processes in different plants.

A good deal is known as to genes controlling differences in the carbohydrates, especially the reserve polysaccharides. The first to be investigated genetically was Mendel's recessive giving wrinkled cotyledons in *Pisum sativum*. This was shown by Bridel and Bourdouil (1932) and Tanret (1935) to substitute stachyose for starch. Table 10 (after Bridel and Bourdouil) suggests that in the

TABLE 10

Stage	Round			Wrinkled		
	Sucrose	Stachyose	Starch	Sucrose	Stachyose	Starch
IV ..	4·3	0	7·5	2·9	0·3	3·2
V ..	0·8	1·9	16·8	3·0	0·6	4·3
VI ..	0·2	2·5	20·6	2·9	1·0	7·2
Dry ..	? 0	? < 6·0	34·6	2·2	11·4	19·8

Quantities in gm/kilo. Stage IV is one where the pod is first oval, at stage VI it is yellow. The round peas alone were studied in earlier stages. They contained some sucrose and starch, but no stachyose. Reducing sugar (? glucose) was present in amounts always less than 1 gm/kilo, and disappeared completely in the dry round peas, while 0·15 gm/kilo remained in the wrinkled. The amounts of sucrose and stachyose in the dried round peas are unknown, since they contain some substance giving a reducing sugar with emulsin other than stachyose or manninotriose.

wrinkled forms there is a partial block to starch synthesis so that a good deal of stachyose (a tetrasaccharide containing two glucose and two galactose residues) and a little sucrose accumulate. It would clearly be of the greatest interest to investigate the enzymes, particularly the phosphorylases and starch-forming enzymes, of these varieties, and to compare the starches by modern methods. Some at least of the starch in normal peas seems to originate from the galactose residues of stachyose, but the conversion of one hexose to the other can hardly be the only process blocked.

The work of Cameron and Teas (1948) on *Zea mays* shows how complicated the situation may well be (Table 11). In maize the endosperm is a triploid tissue, receiving two sets of maternal and one of paternal genes. The same genes, which in the triploid condition determine the nature of the polysaccharide of the endosperm, act in the haploid condition on that of the pollen grains, the two

TABLE 11

Composition of dried endosperm in maize

Su genes	Number of Du genes	% Starch	Nicotinic acid $\times 10^6$
3	3	80·7	21·7
3	2	77·7	22·3
2	3	76·0	21·4
2	2	79·6	23·5
3	1	72·7	22·4
1	3	69·7	22·2
2	1	71·8	29·4
1	2	70·3	25·5
1	1	58·6	29·4
3	0	51·5	44·3
2	0	42·0	46·2
1	0	33·6	51·6
0	3	32·2	56·3
0	2	30·0	48·2
0	1	27·2	50·4
0	0	19·2	56·7

pairs of meiotic products staining differently with iodine. As judged by eye, at least one of two dominant genes *Su* and *Du* are needed to produce a starchy endosperm with a smooth seed, and though the total carbohydrate is roughly constant, the sugar content may rise sharply at the dividing line. The nicotinic acid was estimated by biological assay, and curiously enough agrees much better with the visual judgement of the nature of the pea than does the starch content. Preliminary results showed that thiamine varied even more, from $0 \cdot 18$ to $0 \cdot 98 \times 10^{-6}$, in the same direction, and biotin had a similar trend. These results show clearly that the different types of carbohydrate are indices of far-reaching biochemical differences which will require very thorough investigation.

A little is known on lipid metabolism. In maize Mangelsdorf and Fraps (1931) found that the yellow colour of the endosperm was mainly due to zeaxanthin, and proportional to the number of *Y* genes in the endosperm. The same is true for β-carotene (Table 12).

The sharp proportionality should perhaps act as a warning as to the interpretation of such results. It certainly does not indicate that zeaxanthin and carotene are primary gene products. It does suggest

TABLE 12

Number of Y genes	β-carotene $\times 10^{-6}$
3	4·50
2	3·00
1	1·35
0	0·03

that we are dealing with a process in which the amount of catalyst formed by the gene Y is a limiting factor.

In the tomato (*Lycopersicum esculentum*) Went, Rosen and Zechmeister (1942) stated that the gene R for red flesh caused the appearance of lycopenes, which are absent in rr fruits, and increased the amount of carotene about ten-fold. Mackinney and Jenkins (1952) carried the analysis further. Lycopene includes a group of isomers, and pro-lycopene. They found that RR and Rr plants make much more carotenes and more phytofluene than rr, but a recessive gene t increases the amount of carotenes at the expense of lycopenes in RR and Rr plants, but allows the synthesis of an appreciable amount of lycopenes, mainly prolycopene, in rr plants, along with a little phytofluene. In particular $RRtt$ plants make ζ and ψ-carotenes which are almost, if not quite, absent in other genotypes. The details given are most interesting, but it is not yet possible to state what processes are controlled by these genes.

Cryptostegia grandiflora forms rubber, while *C. madagascariensis* accumulates an ester of the triterpene lupeol. Wildman, Abegg, Elder and Hendriks (1946) found that rubber formation was dominant, and attribute the difference to a single gene.

Finally Teas and Anderson (1951) find that in a recessive fluorescent maize mutant induced by the Bikini atom bomb, the fluorescence is due to anthranilic acid, which is present in about 1000 times the normal concentration. As the plants are apparently healthy, either the path to tryptophan synthesis from this substance (assuming a pathway similar to that in Neurospora) is not wholly blocked, or there is an alternative pathway.

A large number of lethal and semi-lethal chlorophyll-less mutants have been studied. In *Zea mays* normal chloroplast formation requires the compresence of genes at at least fifteen autosomal loci; and genes at perhaps as many more are needed for full greenness. The homozygous recessives die, though they can often be kept alive on sugar; but they grow till their reserves are exhausted, so there is little wrong with their general metabolism. This at least suggests that chlorophyll synthesis is a very complex process. Attempts to elucidate the biochemical differences between different chlorophyll-less mutants have met with small success.

One of the greatest gaps in our knowledge relates to the odours of flowers. These have a precise biochemical basis. They are very variable between species, and somewhat so within a species. They are of very great biological importance in attracting insects, and therefore of evolutionary importance. They are in some cases economically important, but as a field for biochemical and genetical research they have been greatly neglected.

An equally interesting problem is that of self-sterility. In many plants there is a series of allelomorphs, S^1, S^2, S^3, etc., such that the pollen tubes carrying S^1 cannot grow in the styles of plants carrying the same gene, such as S^1S^2 or S^1S^3. For fertilization to occur, the pollen tube must carry a "foreign" gene, and presumably a "foreign" gene product, the exact opposite of the situation as regards tissue grafts in higher animals. It is tempting to suppose that we are concerned with colloidal gene products of the same kind of molecular size as the antigens.* If so, a single species can produce any of over fifty different ones.

---

* Lewis (1952) has shown that in one species they are antigenic.

CHAPTER VI

Biochemical Genetics of Higher Animals, Including Man

Since most colour differences are biochemical differences, though a few are structural, the data of elementary genetics contain, implicitly, a great deal of biochemical information. Until, however, the nature of the pigments is known, biochemists can learn little from such data. In consequence a large fraction of all the data on animal biochemical genetics are based on the study of human biochemical abnormalities. These have been discovered for different reasons. Firstly, because they gave rise to pain, weakness, or death, like cystinuria or phenylketonuria. Secondly, because they produced almost harmless but obvious abnormality, like the blackening of the urine of alkaptonurics. Thirdly, because they simulated the biochemical symptoms of a more serious condition, like pentosuria. Fourthly, like β-aminoisobutyricaciduria, they have been found in the course of laboratory work on apparently normal people. Family investigations (cf. Harris, 1953) have then disclosed their genetic basis.

The few data which we possess on insect biochemical genetics were mostly arrived at as follows. In *Drosophila melanogaster* and other insects mosaics are occasionally produced in which different parts of the body have different genetic compositions. The commonest cause is the elimination at an early cleavage division of the sex-determining X chromosome, giving an insect in which some tissues contain two such chromosomes, and are female, others only one, so that they are male. These tissues develop almost independently. Instead of sex hormones penetrating the whole body as in vertebrates, they can (at least in *Habrobracon juglandis*) diffuse through a few cells only. The same is true of most other biochemical characters. There are, for example, sex-linked recessive genes for white eye and yellow cuticle. If the chromosome containing their normal dominant allelomorphs is lost in the development of a heterozygous female, one eye of a Drosophila may be the normal dark red, the other white or half white, patches of cuticle may be yellow, and similarly for most other genes. This does not hold for a few genes, notably the sex-linked recessive *vermilion*, which suppresses the yellow pigment of the eye, leaving a scarlet. Here the two eyes of a fly are always of the same colour. Further, an eye rudiment from a *vermilion* stock transplanted into a normal larva develops the normal colour, and a normal testis transplanted into a *vermilion* larva will restore a normal coloration to the eyes of the imago derived from it. Clearly some normal tissues produce a diffusible substance which can be utilized by eyes not containing the normal allelomorph of *vermilion* to make pigment. Another recessive, *cinnabar*, behaves in the same way. As the result of extensive work by Beadle, Ephrussi, Kikkawa, Butenandt, Weidel, and many others, summarized by Caspari (1949), it turns out that the yellow pigment missing in *vermilion*, *cinnabar*, and similar eyes, is a group of ommatins (Becker, 1942) consisting of a tryptophan derivative, attached to various proteins. The diffusible substances are kynurenine and 3-hydroxykynurenine, the blocks in *vermilion* and *cinnabar* being between tryptophan and kynurenine, kynurenine and 3-hydroxykynurenine (Butenandt, Weidel, Weichert and Derjugin, 1943). Free tryptophan accumulates in *vermilion* Drosophila (Green, 1947).

Similar mutants are known in other insects. Caspari (1949, and earlier) worked with the moth *Ephestia Kuhniella*. This has a recessive mutant blocking ommatin synthesis at the same point as *vermilion* in Drosophila. The recessives contain more tryptophan than normal, both in their non-protein nitrogen and their protein nitrogen (Butenandt and Albrecht, 1952), and some of their proteins appear to be antigenically different from the normal. Rudkin and Schultz (1949) devised a minimal medium for *Drosophila melanogaster* which contains various amino-acids, including tryptophan. When the amount of tryptophan falls below a certain level there is considerable larval mortality, but the survivors produce more or less vermilion-eyed flies. On such a medium genetically *vermilion* flies survive better than normal. They do not "waste" the small available amounts of tryptophan in making non-essential pigments.

This is analogous to Macdonald and Pontecorvo's (p. 30) findings, and is a means by which unused biochemical capacities may be lost as a result of natural selection rather than a Lamarckian process. For in a population short of tryptophan and containing *vermilion* genes these would spread, so that the failure to produce ommatin originally mainly due to the diet would become genetically fixed.

It is surprising that even one case of a nutritional need (auxotrophism) of the Neurospora type is known in insects. However, the method by which it was discovered may enable the discovery of numerous similar cases. The inversion In(2LR)40D in *Drosophila melanogaster*, in which the central portion of the third chromosome is inverted relative to the ends, is most readily detected either by microscopical examination of the chromosomes or by its interference with normal crossing over. It also produces somatic effects which depend on the state of the culture medium. The most conspicuous is disarrangement of the eye facets. Hinton, Ellis, and Noyes (1951) found that these are "cured" if the larvae are grown in a medium containing plenty of hydrolysed nucleic acid. Normal *Drosophila melanogaster* grows on a medium containing sucrose, 13 amino-acids, cholesterol, lecithin, and vitamins. The addition of nucleic acid speeds up growth and raises the survival from 63% to 74%. On the other hand In(2LR)40D dies on the synthetic medium, while 73% survive when nucleic acid is added. It is found that adenine, or adenine nucleoside or nucleotide were equally effective, whilst guanine allowed a few individuals to develop. These flies are, therefore, "adenineless" presumably because two loci concerned in adenine synthesis have been separated. Similar reactions to diet are not at all uncommon with Drosophila structural mutants, though a few show the opposite behaviour, abnormalities being more marked if large amounts of yeast are added to the diet; but geneticists prefer to work with mutants whose manifestation does not depend on trace constituents in the diet. This is not a mere symptom of laziness. It is much easier to feed rats than Drosophila larvae on a diet deficient in a given vitamin or other constituent. This is because the normal diet contains live yeast, and to rear a batch of larvae on a deficient diet, it is necessary that the bottles in which they are bred and the flies put into them should be completely sterile. The larvae burrow into the food and cannot be transferred to fresh food like rats. At the conclusion of the experiment each bottle must be checked for mycological and bacteriological sterility at the end of a week or more.

Many pigmentary mutants are known in birds. Their genetics and biochemistry are completely different. Thus the feathers of the normal budgerigar (*Melopsittacus undulatus*) are mostly green. They contain melanin and an ether-soluble pigment. One recessive blocks the formation of the yellow pigment, giving blue birds, the blue colour being apparently "structural." Several others block melanin formation, giving yellow birds with normal or red eyes.

E

A white bird is always a double recessive, which has lost both ether-soluble pigment and melanin. On the other hand, in the domestic fowl (*Gallus domesticus*) the yellow feather pigment is a "phaeo-melanin" derived from aromatic amino-acids. The genetical control of pigment is not unlike that of the water-soluble flower pigments. Some genotypes, like the Light Sussex and Cuckoo Leghorn, have black pigment but no yellow, others, like the Pile bantams, have yellow and no black. In the dominant whites the formation of both pigments is inhibited by independent genes, but in several different types of recessive white the formation of both pigments is blocked, and the genetical evidence makes it clear that they are biochemically related. Besides melanin, a fowl's legs may or may not have yellow pigment. On dissection the yellow-legged fowls are found to have yellow pigment in all their fat. The pigment appears to be xantho-phyll, and is inhibited by a dominant gene acting in the same way as that of rabbits described in Chapter I.

In mammals, although the exact composition of the hair pigments is not known, much quantitative work has been done, mainly by Wright (1949), Russell (1949) and Russell and Rusell (1948). There appear to be three chemically different types of pigment, namely yellow, brown, and black; but brown and black are probably alter-natives, only one being formed in a given animal. Colour differences depend on the amounts of these pigments and their arrangements, both on the coat and within individual hairs.

Genes which affect the colour of mouse hairs are known at at least twenty-four different loci (Grüneberg, 1952). At eight of these loci there are genes with highly specific effects on other characters. Some of the remainder have measurable but non-specific effects on growth. Two of the colour mutants (one, *mi*, causing absence of all pigment, the other, *gl*, absence of yellow only) also cause inactivity of the osteoclasts, leading to characteristic skeletal abnormalities. One, *W*, causes a macrocytic, another, *f*, a microcytic anaemia. *Va* causes gross disturbances of locomotion, *pa* minor disturbances due to the absence of otoliths. *Sp* causes prenatal death with spina bifida, and A^Y when homozygous prenatal death before implanta-tion. Clearly many of these genes, like the gene for phenylketonuria in man, which also lightens the hair colour, affect other processes more important than pigment formation. A^Y when heterozygous has a huge effect on weight, mainly by encouraging fat formation. Females increase in weight by 62% but their body length also in-creases by 5%. Some other colour genes increase or decrease body length by 1–3%, and may do so even when heterozygous and with no visible effect on the hair colour. It is clear, then, that if we understood the biochemical genetics of hair pigmentation fully, we should also have information on the developmental biochemistry of the bones, blood, and nervous system at least. Since two different genes affect the osteoclasts specifically, it is clear that these cells must share some metabolic peculiarities with the hair-forming cells. On the other hand pigment formation as such is irrelevant. Albinos (cc) do not differ measurably from normals in weight or viability under laboratory conditions. Not all these genes are at all directly concerned in pigment formation. Thus "blue" mice differ from black in having larger pigment granules, and hence a smaller absorbing surface, but have rather more black and yellow pigments than blacks. Perhaps they lack a surface-active substance which breaks up large granules. It is intelligible that such a biochemical difference may also be responsible for their slightly larger bones. Again, the genes for piebaldness probably inhibit the migration of pigment-forming cells from the neural crest. I am inclined to doubt whether much more than eight of the mouse colour genes (a, b, c, gl, mi, p, pa, and ru) are directly concerned in pigment synthesis.

A further point is important. Among the few genetic differences between related mammalian and amphibian subspecies and species which have been isolated are rather small changes in the activity of some of these colour genes, doubtless reflecting deeper changes in metabolism. We are, therefore, studying biochemical evolution as well as biochemical variation.

Surprisingly little is known about the chemistry of melanin formation in different genotypes. Normal mouse skins possess an insoluble (or difficultly soluble) enzyme, dopa-oxidase whose amount, or activity, can be measured by the rate at which it produces black pigment from "dopa," 3-4-dioxyphenylalanine. This enzyme is absent in the white parts of pigmented mice and in albinos. Its activity is much reduced by some allelomorphs of c, namely c^{ch}, c^{e}, and their heterozygotes with one another and c (Russell and Russell, 1948). This reduction runs parallel with a reduction of yellow pigment (phaeomelanin) but not of black or brown pigment (eumelanin). Whatever dopa-oxidase is doing in mouse skins, it is not oxidizing 3-4-dioxyphenylalanine, though it is very probably concerned in some phase of the production of yellow pigment from a precursor.

Foster (1951), confirming the earlier work of Onslow, discovered that mouse skin contains a true tyrosinase, and also a tryptophan oxidase. He worked with the skin of young mice, powdered under deep freezing. The skin of whites (cc) and the unpigmented parts of the skin of piebald (ss) mice had no tyrosinase activity. That of yellows had a very weak activity. In fact, "yellow" mice often form some black pigment. The skin of black mice had a powerful tyrosinase activity at pH $6\cdot8$, specific for L-tyrosine. The activity was about doubled by $0\cdot6\%$ iodoacetamide, and trebled by about $0\cdot005$ M $CuCl_2$. It could be prevented by phenylthiourea. The uptake amounted to about 5 atoms O per molecule of tyrosine. Dark pigment was formed. Brown skin showed a lesser but still strong tyrosinase activity, and probably inhibited the black skin enzyme. Yellow skin certainly did so. On the other hand the white skin of piebalds seemed to be activated by black skin extracts. That of albino skin was not. Brown agouti skin (giving brown hairs with yellow bands) took up O_2 after a latent period of about 4 hours, or at once if copper or iodoacetamide were added.

Yellow skin contained a powerful tryptophanase, also stereochemically specific. Stoichiometric data are not given, but yellow pigment was formed. Black and brown skins had a less effect, albino skin only after a latent period. This activity is not enhanced by copper, and somewhat depressed by iodoacetamide. Unfortunately yellow pigmentation in mice is due to a dominant gene A^Y, lethal when homozygous, and it cannot be assumed that the recessive yellows in the guinea-pig or rabbit would behave in the same way. In fact one may guess that such yellow skins would not contain tyrosinase, but would not inhibit it unless they carried the gene A giving yellow bands on black hairs. Similarly it is possible that Foster's albino mice carried the gene A, and that albinos not carrying it would have behaved differently. The use of iodoacetamide was suggested by the discovery of Rothman, Krysa, and Smiljanic (1946) that human (European) skin contains an inhibitor of potato tyrosinase, the inhibition being removed by iodoacetamide, and probably depending on sulphydryl groups.

Foster's paper clearly opens a new chapter in the subject. Further, since mammalian tyrosinase has not yet been obtained in solution, it offers the most hopeful method of fractionating it so that the different stages may be studied. The field is now wide open. Among the obvious questions (which Foster may well be answering as I write) are:

Which skin powders, if any, will act on kynurenine, 3-hydroxykynurenine or 3-hydroxyanthranilic acid? Which, if any, will catalyse the oxidation of 5-6-dihydroxyindole-2-carboxylic acid to the corresponding orthoquinone? Can we catalyse the oxidation of tyrosine and tryptophan with mixtures of the skins of albino mice and the white parts of piebald mice, as we can produce full-coloured mice by crossin g them? Are the inhibitors heat stable and dialysable? Can they be isolated? Would enough B.A.L. turn a black mouse yellow?

Let us now turn to Wright's quantitative work. He hydrolysed defatted guinea-pig (*Cavia porcellus*) hair in boiling HCl, removed the chloride, boiled with ·22N KOH, and estimated pigment colorimetrically. The standard error of a single sample was 3–5%, but groups of twenty gave quite accurate results. He worked mainly with non-agouti animals, that is to say with uniform rather than banded hairs, using the following genes:

C, c^k, c^d, c^r, c^a, all allelomorphs, the lowest being almost white.
E, e. ee animals have practically no black or brown hair pigment.
P, p. p dilutes hair colour, and gives a pink eye.
F, f. ff animals have dilute hair colour at birth, which fades further
   with age.
B, b. bb animals have brown pigment instead of black.

These genes give 1215 genotypes, but the number distinguishable is much less both because of dominance and because many are nearly white. The C alleles have quite different effects on yellow pigment and on black and brown. For yellow the order is

C, $c^k = c^d$, $c^r = c^a$. If $C = 100$, $c^k = c^d = 20$, $c_r = c_a = 0$,
for black
C, c^k, c^r, c^d, c^a. If $C = 100$, $c^k = 72$, $c^r = 42$, $c^d = 37$, $c_a = 0$
and for brown
If $C = 100$, $c^k = 82$, $c^r = 63$, $c^d = 63$, $c^a = 0$.

In each case c^a produces no appreciable amount of pigment. These results are most easily explained if each allelomorph produces an enzyme, and these enzymes differ in their relative specificities as regards the precursors of the two types of pigment, one being a derivative of tyrosine, the other of tryptophan. The figures given are amounts of pigment produced by one gene along with c^a. Two active genes together produce an additive effect if each has a small effect, and somewhat less than additive (e.g. $c^k c^d = 80$ for black pigment) if each has a larger effect. This is what we should expect if the immediate effects of the enzymes were additive, but their products were later transformed by another enzyme with a Michaelis constant less than its substrate concentration. P and F control other stages in the formation of melanin. Remarkably, $PPbb$ produces less brown pigment than $Ppbb$ in presence of C. This suggests that one of the enzymes concerned has an optimum substrate concentration, like many lipases and some oxidases, and can be inhibited by excess of substrate.

Wright's papers must be read for a detailed account of these interactions. They leave no doubt that the biochemical account will be extremely complicated. The amounts of pigment produced by various genotypes depends on their age and temperature. Some genotypes darken with age, others fade. The full account will include the biochemical action of all the colour genes.

With these examples before us, we can briefly discuss multiple allelomorphism. A number of cases are known where several mutants at the same locus (or very close together) determine the production of different amounts of what seems to be the same end product (e.g. yellow pigment in mice, eye pigments in Drosophila) or different degrees of development of the same organ (e.g. the wings in Drosophila or the leaf margin in *Primula sinesis*). Wright (1916) and Goldschmidt (1916) regarded each allelomorphic gene as responsible for a particular rate of development, and Wright thought that the different genes produced different amounts of the *same* enzyme. Goldschmidt (1938 and earlier) had developed the idea of rate control in great detail. The book referred to is of great value, but most of the information in it antedates the application of exact biochemical methods.

So long as only one character was studied, it was naturally found that multiple allelomorphs could be placed in a definite order, and their action was usually found to be more or less additive. This led me to the view (Haldane, 1920) expressed in the following sentence (cf. Wright, 1916): "The precise nature of their activity is uncertain, but in some cases we have very strong evidence that they [genes] produce definite quantities of enzymes, and that members of a series of multiple allelomorphs produce the same enzyme in different quantities." This is vague. "Produce" is more precise than Cuénot's (1903) "doit contenir en puissance," and less so than "catalyses the formation of." This, however, will appear equally vague to our successors. The statement is also probably untrue. I am not ashamed of this. The hypothesis has had a heuristic value, and is susceptible of disproof. It has not, in fact, yet been disproved in a single case by isolating the enzymes produced by different allelomorphs and comparing their properties *in vitro* as those of haemoglobins have been compared, but attempts should be made to disprove it, and would probably succeed in doing so. When several characters were studied at once, for example black and yellow pigments in guinea-pigs, or bristle length on different parts of the body in Drosophila, it was soon found that the order in which the allelomorphs were ranked could be different for each character studied. This could be explained in several ways. Each gene might be producing a series of enzymes with different absolute specificities, or hormones stimulating growth in different parts of the body, in different amounts, but it is easier to imagine that the different genes produce qualitatively different products, each with a range of specificity, like esterases or adrenaline-like bases.

Muller (1932) classified mutant genes as amorphs if they are inactive, hypomorphs if they are doing the same as the wild-type gene but less intensely, hypermorphs if they are doing the same but more intensely, antimorphs if they are competing with the wild-type gene, and neomorphs if they are controlling some process with which the wild-type gene is not concerned. By making up Drosophila containing extra fragments of chromosome with the gene in question he was able to classify genes in this way. Thus one *bobbed* gene produces very short bristles, two produce somewhat longer ones, three nearly the normal length; hence *bobbed* is a hypomorph.

However, the same gene, for example the gene for "Japanese" or "Harlequin" pattern in rabbits, can be hypomorphic in respect of one action and hypermorphic in another. This is quite intelligible if we think in terms of qualitatively different gene products.

It is thus plausible that different allelomorphs make chemically different primary products, for example enzymes with the same prosthetic group attached to different proteins, and their interaction in heterozygotes is a biochemical matter, often different in different organs. This could still be so even if, as is true in some cases and may be in many, so called multiple allelomorphs are really what Bateson called spurious allelomorphs, being due to mutations at loci so close together on a chromosome that they can co-operate in synthesis (see Chapter IX).

Certain facts about enzymes support the point of view here developed. All yeast saccharases have the same optimum pH, but their Michaelis constants differ considerably (Kühn, 1923). According to Willstätter, Kühn and Sobotka (1923) those of β-glucosidases from plants of the same genus differ even more, and their affinities for different substrates do not vary in parallel. Haldane (1930, pp. 43–45) discussed the matter. It would clearly be worth while taking up the problem once more with genetically characterized yeasts or better with Neurospora strains. However, exact work of this type on enzymes has perhaps gone out of fashion.

The cuticular pigment of insects is due to the action of enzymes in the cuticle on a phenolic acid found in the haemolymph, and the differences due to various genes (e.g. *yellow* and *ebony* in *Drosophila melanogaster*) seem to depend on these enzymes rather than on the amount of substrate available for them. Kalmus (1941) showed that the darker cuticles are less permeable to water and other substances than the lighter ones. Thus yellow flies lose water more quickly than brown and black ones in dry air, and after drying over sulphuric acid regain weight more quickly when replaced in normal air. The skin colour of insects may, therefore, be adapted to differences of humidity as well as to concealment from enemies and other forms of positive and negative "communication." The darkening of insect cuticles is a process similar to the tanning of leather.

We know rather little of human colour genetics, but we know a good deal of the activities of two genes which are, incidentally, colour genes. These genes, discussed later, cause phenylketonuria and alkaptonuria. Phenylketonurics, who cannot oxidize phenylalanine and related compounds in the para position, have light hair. Alkaptonurics, who cannot oxidize homogentisic acid, not only produce a urine which blackens on standing, but form pigment in their sclerotics and their cartilages, which may become hard and brittle. The analogy with insect cuticular pigmentation is obvious.

I therefore begin with a case where the genetics and physiology are fairly clear. Most dogs (and other mammals) excrete much more allantoin than uric acid. Normal dogs excrete about $0 \cdot 2\%$ of their urinary nitrogen as uric acid, Dalmatian coach dogs 2–3%; nevertheless they excrete about twice as much allantoin as uric acid. Various authors failed to find a diminished content of uricase, which oxidizes uric acid to allantoin, in their organs. Friedman and Byers (1948) found that in all dogs the allantoin clearance is equal to the creatinine clearance. That is to say, they excrete all the creatinine and allantoin in about a quarter of the plasma volume passing through their kidneys, which probably means that neither substance is reabsorbed from the glomerular filtrate. Normal dogs have a much lower uric acid clearance, which presumably means that they reabsorb this substance from the filtrate. In Dalmatians the uric acid clearance is the same as the creatinine clearance. In consequence the ratio of uric acid to creatinine in the urine is higher than normal, and about a third of their uric acid is excreted as such before it has had time to be oxidized to allantoin. Thus increased uric acid excretion in dogs is physiologically comparable to renal glycosuria in men. The relatively high uric acid excretion and lack of allantoin in Primates is due to a rise in the renal threshold for uric acid or at least a sluggishness in excreting it, a mutation in the opposite direction to that found in the Dalmatian dogs.

The most extensive data on animal biochemical genetics relate to man. They are satisfactory because even minor and rare abnormalities can be detected, if they cause ill-health or abnormal appearance, or if they simulate the biochemical symptoms of well-known diseases. For example, routine life insurance tests detect the presence of any substance in urine which reduces one of the reagents used in testing for glucose. Moreover, human physiology is relatively well known, and medical techniques are highly developed. On the other hand genetical experiments are impossible, so that we can no more say, except in special cases, that the abnormality in two families is due to mutations at the same locus, than we can in asexual bacteria or fungi. In particular we do not know what the homozygous forms of rare human "dominants" are like. Thus if two renal glycosurics marry, it may be that on an average three-quarters of their children are ordinary renal glycosurics. It may be that the homozygous quarter are so severely affected as to die young or even prenatally. Nor, of course, can we perform drastic experiments, such as transplanting or perfusing organs, or placing patients on grossly deficient diets.

I shall begin with a group of abnormalities in which a substance is found in the urine which is not known to occur in normal urines, or occurs in them in quantities of the order of a tenth, a hundredth, or less, of that characteristic of the abnormality. It would be satisfactory if we could divide these abnormalities sharply into two classes. In one the renal threshold would be absent or abnormally low, so that the substance was excreted, though its concentration in the blood was normal or slightly subnormal. In the other the substance in question would be inadequately or not at all utilized, either by all the tissues or by an important organ such as the liver. Its concentration in the blood would be supernormal, and the kidney would excrete it just as the kidney of a normal man would do if perfused with blood containing it in high concentration. It is generally believed that renal glycosuria and diabetes mellitus are examples of these two classes.

There are, however, several objections to such a view. If, owing to a gene substitution, say the lack of a pair of normal genes in a pair of homologous maternal and paternal chromosomes, the renal tubule cells cannot absorb a particular metabolite, say cystine, from the glomerular filtrate, it would not be surprising if, for example, the liver cells, which lack the same pair of genes, were at least somewhat inefficient at absorbing cystine from the plasma. Thus a failure of renal function could be a mark of a general metabolic abnormality. Secondly, the evidence as to plasma concentrations is inadequate or even non-existent in some cases, for example xyloketosuria and β-aminoisobutyricaciduria. Finally, the evidence may exist but be ambiguous. Neuberger, Rimington and Wilson (1947) found that an alkaptonuric had a very low content of homogentisic acid in his blood, but excreted it in greater amounts than could be explained on the basis of filtration and reabsorption. This would suggest that alkaptonuria is a renal abnormality, but the fact of ochronosis (pigment deposition in cartilage) makes it clear either that alkaptonurics have an abnormal amount of this substance in other tissues than the kidney, or at least that the other tissues are somehow handicapped in dealing with it. Much of the urinary homogentisic acid may be a product of the kidneys' metabolism. Although, therefore, I shall take the provisional view that alkaptonuria is a metabolic block rather than a lowering of a renal threshold, I fully realize both that this is only a working hypothesis, and that the alternatives are not exclusive.

Provisionally, then, the following abnormalities appear to be due to enhanced renal excretion. As asterisk denotes that Harris (1953) gives a bibliography and often original observations, along with a fuller discussion than my own.

Renal glycosuria.*—This, so far, appears to be due to an autosomal dominant. The renal threshold for glucose is below 1 gm/litre, and glucose is excreted after meals and sometimes even when fasting. The affected persons doubtless waste a little glucose, but enjoy good health.

β-aminoisobutyricaciduria.*—This acid is found in small amounts in most or all human urines. About 10% of normal human beings excrete 100–300 mgm per day. This may turn out to be a metabolic abnormality. The data suggest that it is an autosomal recessive. The acid is perhaps derived from the catabolism of thymine.

Classical cystinuria.*—The patients excrete cystine, arginine, and lysine, each in quantities of about half a gram daily. The plasma cystine is, if anything, lowered. Dr. Harris has very strong unpublished evidence that the condition is due to recessive genes at at least two different autosomal loci.

Juvenile Fanconi's syndrome.*—The patients excrete not only cystine, but excessive quantities of glycine, alanine, threonine, the leucines, valine, proline, lysine, arginine, histidine, phenylalanine, and tyrosine, besides glucose and phosphate. Autosomal recessive.

Adult Fanconi's syndrome.*—As in the juvenile form, but probably due to a different gene. It is quite possible that these are to be regarded as metabolic diseases rather than renal defects, particularly because cystine crystals have been found in the tissues in the juvenile, though not the adult, Fanconi's syndrome.

Classical cystinuria gives rise to calculus formation, Fanconi's syndrome to intractable rickets or osteomalacia; but at least in adults it may be symptomless over periods of years. The plasma cystine does not seem to be raised, and the kidney is probably responsible for the cystine excretion. On the other hand there are several other conditions characterized by excessive cystine excretion in which there is good evidence of a metabolic upset. These are dealt with later.

Hyperuricaemia.*—This condition can be due to excessive uric acid production, as in leukaemia. If so, it is accompanied by greatly enhanced excretion. The mean plasma urate is about 40–50 mg/litre in normal men, and 30–40 mg/litre in women, though it is very variable. In genetically determined hyperuricaemia it is about 100 mg/litre with a normal urinary excretion rate. Some hyperuricaemics, mostly males, develop gout. Hyperuricaemia seems to be due to an autosomal dominant. The fraction of the hyperuricaemics who actually develop gout is small, and the onset or otherwise of gout probably depends on the steroid hormones, among other things.

These facts make it clear that renal tubular reabsorption is a most complicated process, and not the mere reabsorption of an "optimal fluid." Further, since we know that water reabsorption is controlled by a hormone produced by the posterior pituitary, and sodium reabsorption by a hormone of the adrenal cortex, it is possible that, for example, Fanconi's syndrome may have a hormonal basis, the renal tubule cells behaving abnormally not because of the abnormality of genes in their own nuclei, but because of the abnormality of genes in the adrenal cortex, the anterior pituitary, the hypothalamus, or some other organ. Even if the abnormality is due to genes in the tubules, it could act by altering their sensitivity to a hormone, and the condition might thus be controllable by hormone therapy.

I continue with the discussion of conditions believed to be due to a metabolic block.

The most important of these is diabetes mellitus. The work of Harris (1949, 1950) confirming that of Levit, Pincus and others, leaves no reasonable doubt that this disease is, to some extent, genetically determined. If we call normal people DD, where D is an autosomal gene, then the facts are consistent with the hypothesis that a fair fraction of Dd people become diabetic in middle or late life, while a considerable fraction of dd develop the disease in early life. However, the conditions under which a member of a given geno-type will develop the disease are largely unknown, though they certainly include over-eating. In 1930–32 the Registrar General's Report on Occupational Mortality shows that deaths from this disease were $2 \cdot 0$ times as common among grocers, $2 \cdot 4$ times as common among proprietors of other retail food shops, and $3 \cdot 3$ times as common among innkeepers, as in the general population. This does not mean that diabetes has no genetic basis. It means that persons with diabetic relatives should regard innkeeping as a particularly risky occupation. It is most unlikely that all liability to diabetes is due to a single gene, if only because we know that this disease is due to the upset of a complicated balance between hexokinase (glucose-phosphorylase), one or more pituitary hormones, and insulin. A gene affecting the production of any of these substances could bring on diabetes. The example of diabetes should show that the one gene-one enzyme hypothesis is unlikely to be of universal validity even in bacteria, and becomes less and less plausible in more highly integrated organisms. In most cases of diabetes the deficiency which causes a partial block in the phosphorylation of glucose is probably not an inadequacy of hexokinase but a shortage of insulin, which appears to inhibit an inhibitor of this enzyme.

Glycogen disease,* or hepatosplenomegalia glycogenica, which is perhaps due to an autosomal recessive, is characterized by excessive deposition of glycogen in the liver, and hypoglycaemia which may become severe on fasting. Growth is slow and early death common. The glycogen is stable even after death, though readily broken down by normal liver. van Creveld (1952) suggests that there is a deficiency of glucose-6-phosphatase.

In fructosuria* about 10 to 20% of the fructose ingested as such or as sucrose is excreted. The normal rise in respiratory quotient does not occur after fructose ingestion, but the blood fructose rises higher than usual. However, most fructose is used, and the condition, which is an autosomal recessive, is not at all serious.

A large number of cases of pentosuria* have been described, and there is little doubt that the condition is due to an autosomal recessive gene. A number of different sugars have, in the past, been described as present, and even though, for example, authors who described it as d-ribose later withdrew the claim, the sugar persists in bibliographies. After the work of Enklewitz and Lasker (1935) there seems little doubt that the sugar is l-xyloketose (osazones with the same rotatory power were earlier ascribed to d-xyloketose). The excretion is fairly independent of diet, but Enklewitz and Lasker showed that from 21·% to 36% of ingested d-glucuronic acid was excreted as l-xyloketose, though such a transformation is certainly surprising. They were unable to find this sugar in the urines of normal people who had been given glucuronic acid. Provisionally it seems best to assume that all pentosuria is xyloketosuria, and that this condition is due to a block in one of the possible pathways of catabolism of glucuronic acid. It is clearly plausible that a molecule with different active groups at each end should be broken down in different ways.

Galactosuria,* a similar probably recessive condition, is much more dangerous. It appears that very little of the ingested galactose can be utilized, and the ingestion produces severe illness, including albuminuria and anaemia (Mason and Turner, 1935). This is liable to be fatal to babies, unless they are taken off a diet of milk and given a synthetic mixture containing another sugar. Presumably they should later avoid snails, green peas, and other galactose sources, as well as milk.

The smallest molecule present in unusually large amounts in a genetically determined condition is oxalic acid. Essential oxaluria is probably due to a dominant gene (Gram, 1932). It creates a liability to renal calculi, and metabolic studies on it should be particularly interesting.

Three blocks in the metabolism of the aromatic amino-acids are known.

Phenylketonuria* is an autosomal recessive condition in which up to a gram a day of phenylpyruvic acid, and considerable quantities of the order of 200 mg, of phenylalanine and phenyllactic acid are excreted, along with some phenylacetylglutamine. The plasma and cerebrospinal fluid contain about twenty-five times the normal concentration of phenylalanine. Almost all phenylalanine ingested is excreted in one of these forms within 48 hours, but the proteins contain this substance in normal amounts. The plasma tyrosine rises within half an hour when phenylalanine is fed to a normal individual, but not when it is fed to a phenylketonuric. The most probable block is in the activity of a liver enzyme system which oxidises phenylalanine to tyrosine, but may also act on some of its deaminated products.

Phenylketonurics are generally mentally defective, and always mentally retarded. The reason for this is unknown. The hair pigmentation is reduced, and if phenylketonuria occurred in a laboratory mammal it would be detected as a gene for pigment dilution rather than mental defect. A preliminary and incomplete search among mouse colour mutants has not revealed it. If it is detected in an animal it should be possible to show that such an animal, unlike a normal mammal, is "tyrosineless"—that is to say, requires tyrosine in its diet. For obvious reasons the experiment has not been made on a phenylpyruvic man, but the mutant could probably be so designated, and is in fact sometimes so called in conversation by Dr. Harris, to whom I owe this important analogy.

Only one case of tyrosinosis* has been described, and nothing is known of its genetical determination. The patient excreted tyrosine and p-hydroxyphenylpyruvic acid. He excreted still more if fed with tyrosine, phenylalanine, p-hydroxyphenylpyruvic acid, or 3-4-dihydroxyphenylalanine; and the latter substance and p-hydroxyphenyllactic acid also appeared. He could metabolize homogentisic acid completely. He suffered from a myasthenia gravis, which may or may not have been a consequence of the metabolic abnormality. If so it is not the usual cause of this disease.

Alkaptonuria* was one of the first conditions recognized by Garrod (1909 and earlier) as an autosomal recessive. The condition is usually detected within a few days of birth, as the urine blackens on standing by oxidation. Homogentisic acid is excreted in amounts up to 5 grams or more per day, and 80% or more of the tyrosine and phenylalanine in the diet was converted into homogentisic acid. Small amounts are used for tissue building, pigment formation, hormone formation, and so on. Not only the amino-acids, but phenylpyruvic, phenyllactic and p-hydroxyphenylpyruvic acids are converted fairly quantitatively into homogentisic acid. o- and m-hydroxyphenylalanine, and o- and m-hydroxyphenylpyruvic acids are not, but 2-5-dihydroxyphenylalanine is. Normal human beings can oxidize homogentisic acid, though a dose of 8 gm caused a transient alkaptonuria.

Ravdin and Crandall (1951) found that rats' liver slices convert homogentisic acid into 4-fumaryl-acetoacetic acid, which is then hydrolyzed to fumaric and acetoacetic acids. This is one of the few processes by which a benzene ring is known to be broken in mammals. It will clearly be possible to find out whether this enzyme system exists in alkaptonurics, and if not, which component in it is absent.

Fig. 6 attempts a survey of the reactions concerned in these conditions. Some further arguments in favour of it are given by

FIG. 6

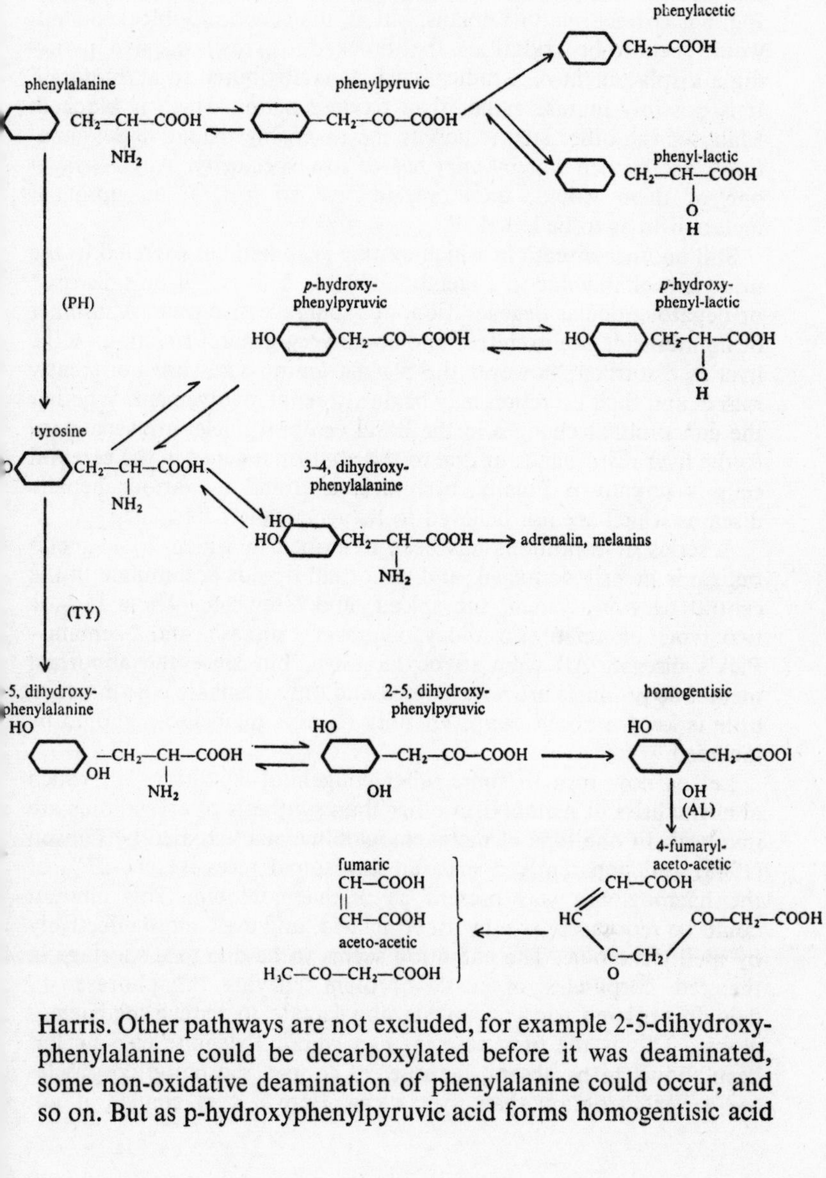

Harris. Other pathways are not excluded, for example 2-5-dihydroxyphenylalanine could be decarboxylated before it was deaminated, some non-oxidative deamination of phenylalanine could occur, and so on. But as p-hydroxyphenylpyruvic acid forms homogentisic acid more slowly than does tyrosine in an alkaptonuric, it seems reasonable to suppose that only tyrosine can be converted to a 2-5-dihydroxy compound, probably by migration of the side chain, and that this is the process blocked in tyrosinosis. It is unlikely that Fig. 6 is correct in all its details, but all the genetically blocked steps would seem to be oxidations, that blocked in tyrosinosis also involving a displacement of a radical such as is attributed to a "mutase." It is possibly mutase rather than oxidase action which is blocked. Many of the other steps, such as the reversible oxidative deaminations, are carried out by enzymes of low specificity. Any block in one of them would, therefore, involve so general an upset of metabolism as to be lethal.

Still another disease in which cystine is sometimes excreted in the urine is probably due to a metabolic block. This is Wilson's disease* or hepatolenticular degeneration, due to a recessive gene. A number of amino-acids are excreted, and some very general function of the liver is disturbed; however the plasma amino-acids are not greatly raised, and their excretion may be due to renal involvement. Whether the concomitant changes in the basal cerebral nuclei are secondary to the liver disturbance or due to the abnormal genes in the cerebral cells is unknown. Finally, cystinuria is found in various hepatic diseases which are not believed to be genetically determined.

A series of conditions has been described in which lipoid metabolism is grossly deranged, and abnormal lipoids accumulate in the central nervous system, the spleen, and elsewhere. These include two types of amaurotic idiocy, Gaucher's disease, and Niemann–Pick's disease. All seem to be recessive, but since the abnormal metabolic products are not excreted and only available post mortem, little is known about them. Possibly retinitis pigmentosa should be included.

Let us now turn to some other congenital conditions, in which abnormalities of metabolism other than synthesis of crystalloids are involved. In one type of methaemoglobinaemia* studied by Gibson (1948) and apparently due to an autosomal recessive, 11–27% of the haemoglobin was present as methaemoglobin. This amount could be reduced *in vivo* by ascorbic acid, and even more effectively by methylene blue. The condition seems to be due to a shortage in the red corpuscles of a flavoprotein enzyme "diaphorase I" dehydrogenating triosephosphate and lactate to reduce methaemoglobin. This is the only case in man where a definite enzyme has been shown to be absent, because, of course, red blood corpuscles are easier to obtain than liver slices. Here a very similar, if not identical, enzyme is presumably present in heart muscle. The condition may thus be more like piebaldness than like albinism. We saw in Chapter II that another type of methaemoglobinaemia was due to an abnormality of the globin part of the haemoglobin molecule. There is probably still a third genetically determined variety.

A good deal of work has been done on abnormalities of porphyrin metabolism both in men and animals, but the conclusions are far from clear. It will be remembered that two types of porphyrins have been found in biological material, series III which is asymmetrical, and is found in normal haem and other prosthetic groups, as well as in chlorophyll, and the symmetrical series I. The whole question of porphyrin classification has, however, been reopened by Nicholas and Rimington's (1951) discovery, along with the long known coproporphyrins with four carboxyl groups and uroporphyrins with eight such groups, of porphyrins which, judged so far mainly from their chromatographic behaviour, had two, three, five, six, and seven carboxyl groups. Two types of genetically determined abnormality can, perhaps, be distinguished. In one type the porphyrins excreted are of Type III. The condition is inherited in man as an irregular dominant. One or more acute attacks occur in middle or late life in which large amounts of uroporphyrin III are excreted. The central nervous system may be fatally involved, but there is no photosensitivity. Besides uroporphyrin III, Nicholas and Rimington found a good deal of the 7-carboxyporphyrin in one case, and smaller amounts of other compounds in others.

The chronic recessive type mainly excretes porphyrins of series I throughout life. Uroporphyrin, coproporphyrin, and the whole range with from 2 to 7 carboxyls have been reported. They are present in various tissues, staining the bones pink, and making the skin light-sensitive, so that it blisters in summer.

A bibliography and some recent results are given by Rimington and Miles (1951). About 60 mg/day of uroporphyrin was excreted, but accompanied by a variety of porphyrins of series I and some of III. Rimington (1936) had fully described a similar case in cattle. Gray, Neuberger and colleagues (1950) have used radioactive isotopes to follow the metabolism of the porphyrins concerned. The patient was fed with N^{15} labelled glycine, which is the sole source of porphyrin nitrogen. The haemoglobin contains only porphyrin III, though porphyrins I are present in the corpuscles. However, the synthesis and destruction of haemoglobin are both disturbed. The bone marrow is overactive and the corpuscles have

F

a short life. This case is of peculiar interest because an abnormal substance seems to be synthesized, though normal men are thought to produce traces of porphyrins of series I. It is difficult to regard congenital porphyria as a mere loss of function. Progressive biochemical evolution must mean the establishment of new types of synthesis. Here we have one which is harmful and unlikely to be used in evolution, but nevertheless suggests how evolution may have occurred.

In several other human congenital abnormalities there is abnormal light sensitivity of the skin, and injections of serum are said to have sensitized normal skin, but no porphyrins have been detected. They presumably have a biochemical basis.

Clearly there are biochemical differences between individuals of a species, and some of these are genetically determined. If they are genetically determined they will appear as differences between mean values in members of pure lines, though the converse is not true. Pure lines of mice have been compared in respect of food requirements and enzyme contents. Some details and a bibliography are given by Grüneberg (1952, pp. 374–377).

Pure lines differ in their requirements of riboflavin and pantothenic acid. As Grüneberg points out, this could be due to differences in their intestinal flora, which certainly exist. It is possible that these could be due to genetically determined differences between the lines which have nothing to do with vitamins. Thus the C57 black strain has fewer Peyer's patches of lymphoid tissue than most others. It also has a high bacterial count in its intestine on a synthetic diet, and a lower riboflavin requirement than a strain with which it was compared. This example shows that even if the difference in riboflavin requirements is genetically determined, it may be so in a very roundabout manner.

One strain has about twice as much xanthine oxidase in its liver as another. Others differ in their liver content of ascorbic acid. The C57 black strain has a serum esterase content about half that of five other strains, and Khanolkar and Chitre (1944) found that this difference was reversed when each was suckled by foster-mothers of the other strain (cf. p. 88). We must, however, remember that young mice presumably receive bacterial flora as well as milk from their foster-mothers; but this fact makes it clear that we cannot assert that these quantitative differences between inbred lines are genetically determined until a genetical analysis has been carried out with suitable tests for milk transmission and bacterial or virus infection. Nevertheless, I have little doubt that some of these differences will prove to be genetically determined, and of these some may depend on a few genes. The study of such genes might be more important both for human hygiene and for the study of evolution than that of the complete losses of function with which this chapter has mainly been concerned, though they would throw less light on paths in intermediary metabolism.

Weir (1949, 1950) reported differences in the pH of the blood in different mouse strains, and attempted to correlate it with disease resistance.

There is no doubt that many of the congenital anomalies of human sensation have a biochemical basis, and certain fairly obvious speculations can be made as to the biochemistry of colour-blindness, night blindness, and day blindness. Examination of retinae from such cases is clearly desirable. However, one case calls for further comment. Harris* describes his own and colleagues' investigation on the taste of the thio-ureas and related compounds. Fox (1932) found that some people regarded phenyl-thio-urea as very bitter, while others cannot taste it. The ability to taste it is thought to be due to a single dominant gene, but this is by no means clearly established. There is, however, no doubt that it is largely genetically determined, and that the distribution of taste thresholds is highly bimodal. If a number of individuals are classified according as they do or do not taste phenyl-thio-urea as bitter, they show similar differences for sixteen other substances, such as thiouracil and thioacetamide, all containing the group

$$= N - C -$$
$$\overset{\|}{S}$$

Every substance so far tried containing this group, except sym-di-o-tolyl thio-urea, has shown this dimorphism, and a variety of others, some containing sulphur in other groupings, have not.

Now all these substances, particularly methyl-thiouracil, inhibit thyroid function, and one, 1-5-vinyl-2-thio-oxazolidine, occurs in turnips. It seemed possible that the difference in taste sensitivity might be correlated with a difference in thyroid response. In fact the percentage of "non-tasters" among patients with nodular goitre is decidedly above that in the general population, but more data are needed before the significance of the difference is established beyond a shadow of doubt.

I close this chapter with a brief account of work which may prove to have opened up a new line in genetical biochemistry. Jucci (1944) and his colleagues have worked on the genetics of the colour of the silk produced by the caterpillars of the silkworm moth *Bombyx mori*. When silk is coloured, the pigment always seems to be derived from the food of the caterpillars, the usual pigments being carotenoids or flavones. The coloration may be uniform, or each fibre may be a chromatogram, coloured at one end and white at the other. The pigments found in silk are always present in the haemolymph, but not conversely. The genetics are complicated, but it appears that some genes, for example one for a carotene-oxidase, determine the destruction of the pigments. Others determine whether or not, if present in the haemolymph, they will appear in the silk. That is to say, they control the permeability of certain membranes. We have already met with genes of this type in man, namely the various genes controlling renal reabsorption. Jucci suggests that such genes may be of considerable importance, and that what are now interpreted as metabolic blocks may turn out to be blocks in membranes. He may well be right.

If the central thesis of this book is correct, all genetically determined variation has a biochemical basis. This basis will only be known when the biochemistry of morphogenesis is understood, but conversely the search for it will help to establish the biochemistry of morphogenesis. A few authors have tried to explain a number of innate structural differences as due to secretion of a hormone in abnormal amounts. This does not seem a very hopeful line. Serious excess or defect of a hormone causes a very general physiological upset. On the other hand, genes are known which alter the threshold of response of tissues to hormones. This is one, but only one, way in which growth is genetically controlled. The most striking is that producing henny feathering in male poultry by reducing the threshold of response of their feather follicles to oestrone and other hormones (Punnett and Bailey, 1921; Deanesley and Parkes, 1937). Numerous differences are known in the response of mouse strains to oestrone (cf. Grüneberg, 1952, pp. 135–136), gonad-stimulating hormone, and insulin. Their genetical basis is hardly known, but it is of interest that in two strains the oestrone threshold of the vagina differs, while that of the mammary glands does not. The genetically determined differences are, therefore, organ-specific or tissue-specific. This is what one would have to postulate if genetically determined differences in the size of organs were partly due to differences in response to hormones.

An insulin-resistant mouse strain can survive no less than 300 times the dose which will kill a more normal strain (Chase, Gunther,

Miller, and Wolffson, 1948). Chase's (1950) data suggest that more than one gene is concerned, and there is little dominance. The blood sugar of these mice is within normal limits.

Grüneberg's monograph refers to eighty-eight papers on mouse endocrinology, mostly concerned with differences which seem to be genetically determined. In only one case (pituitary dwarfism) is a difference known to be due to a single gene. When even a few of them have been adequately analysed, a new chapter in biochemical genetics will have been written.

Extranuclear Influences on Biochemical Activity, Including Training

Once we depart from the study of characters determined by genes we are faced by considerable difficulties. One is the difficulty or impossibility of distinguishing between the transmission of characters determined by self-reproducing extranuclear structures and by viruses. Another is the problem of training in unicellular organisms, which I have deliberately postponed.

The absence or abnormality of chloroplasts in higher plants may be due to nuclear genes. Or all the descendants of abnormal chloroplasts may be abnormal. In this case the inheritance is usually maternal, since it is unusual, though not unknown, for chloroplasts to be transmitted through pollen tubes. In flagellates the chloroplasts are often countable, and different species, when grown in darkness in sugar or other nutrient solution, may display every gradation of behaviour from one satisfying the theoretical views of Weissman to one satisfying those of Lamarck (for references *v.* Lwoff, 1944, p. 83).

Haematococcus pluvialis remains green indefinitely.

Euglena gracilis loses chlorophyll after a few weeks in darkness, but retains eight to ten plastids. Even after fifteen years in darkness it becomes green after a few hours in light. This is like the "training" of bacteria and yeasts.

Euglena mesnili normally possesses about one hundred chloroplasts. In darkness they remain green, but their number falls off, and may fall to one or two after some months. If so, individuals without plastids may be formed at a mitotic division. Unlike plastidless individuals of *Rhizochrysis scherfeli*, which are formed when its single large plastid fails to divide, plastidless *E. mesnili* can reproduce, though they grow slowly, and have never been kept over many generations. Here, then, is a perfect Lamarckian example of irreversible heritable loss of a function through disuse. It is apparently vain to hope that the existence of such a series of organisms will prevent dogmatic assertions both as to the non-existence of this phenomenon and as to its universality. In connection with the comparative anatomy of chloroplasts in higher plants, Metzner's (1952) finding that they contain DNA as well as RNA may not be irrelevant.

Ephrussi (1949 and in the press) investigated a similar case in yeast. Normal yeasts occasionally produce small slowly growing cells, which do not oxidize "nadi" (α-naphthol + p-phenylene diamine) to a characteristic blue colour, as the normal yeast cells do. These cells originate by "mutation," one of a pair being small in about $0 \cdot 4\%$ of divisions. If acriflavine is added to a culture, there is no effect unless cells divide, but mutation occurs at most divisions, and after twenty-four hours less than 1% of the cells are normal. The mutation is irreversible. The mutants lack cytochrome oxidase and succinic dehydrogenase, and, though they can ferment glucose, cannot oxidize it. When a culture of the small form is grown in a normal medium and crossed with the normal, all the spores in an ascus usually give normals, whereas other characters (e.g. "adenineless" producing a red pigment) usually give 1 : 1 segregation. However, about 1% of such spores give small cells. Ephrussi showed conclusively that this was not due to Mendelian segregation of several genes. He later obtained a mutant in which a similar obligatory anaerobiosis was due to a single gene. If the normal yeast cell has nine self-reproducing cytoplasmic particles containing the respiratory enzymes which are distributed at random, we should expect to get 1 cell in 512 without such a particle in binary divisions, and about 1 in 50 in quaternary divisions. If acriflavine prevents the particles from dividing the observed results can be explained. Quite recently Mitchell and Mitchell (1952) have obtained the first cytoplasmically determined mutant in *Neurospora crassa*. This is "*poky*," a slow grower for reasons at present unknown.

In *Paramecium aurelia* some stocks produce "paramecins" which kill other members of the same species. van Wagtendonk (1948) showed that they are desoxyribonucleoproteins. They are spontaneously inactivated at all pH's, though most slowly at $8 \cdot 5$. The inactivation is accelerated by several proteinases and by desoxyribonuclease in presence of Mg^{++} or Mn^{++}. Paramecin is produced by (and may be but is probably not identical with) Feulgen-staining particles called Kappa in the cytoplasm of the killers. A single cell may contain about a thousand of these particles. These will only multiply in presence of a nuclear gene K (cf. Sonneborn, 1947), though they may persist for at least five cells divisions after K has been lost. If animals are kept in a medium where fission is rapid, they may divide more rapidly than the Kappa particles, and finally the large majority cease to be killers. Clearly Kappa may be regarded as a kind of virus, but if so it is peculiar in protecting its hosts against effects which are fatal to "uninfected" individuals. On the other hand, any virus with this peculiar property is clearly favoured by natural selection.

A number of self-propagating cytoplasmic properties are known in higher plants. Some are transmitted purely maternally. Of these again some can be transmitted by grafting. Darlington (1949) and Lysenko (1949) have reviewed this topic, but it does not seem to me that the evidence is at present sufficient to justify the sweeping claims made by either of these authors, though such evidence may be obtained.

In mammals several characters are transmissible by milk. Mammary cancer in mice is due to a virus which is regularly transmitted to the offspring or foster-children through the milk (Bittner, 1937 and later) (for a full bibliography, v. Grüneberg, 1952). However, two points are to be noted. In the first place the mammary cancer virus causes acinar hypertrophy during the first lactation or earlier, while cancer may not develop till much later. Secondly, the age at which cancer develops depends in part on genes transmitted in the ordinary way. The virus is thus not harmful to all mice, and we must be prepared to find harmless characters transmitted in a similar manner.

A case which will doubtless be further investigated was described by Rutman, Dempster, and Turner (1949) and Rutman (1951). Growth rates in animals are in part genetically determined. They may depend in part on the rate at which amino-acids are incorporated into tissue protein. They therefore compared rats of a rapidly growing inbred strain F, and a slower growing strain J. The authors incubated liver slices for two hours with $1 \cdot 33 \ \mu M$ DL-methionine containing radio-sulphur, and isolated methionine sulphur from the protein hydrolysate. Rats of strain F gave about $0 \cdot 4\%$ replacement, strain J about $0 \cdot 27\%$. Most remarkably, however, rats of strain J, when suckled by F mothers, not only grew more quickly (indeed more quickly than either J or F nursed by their own mothers), but incorporated methionine as rapidly as F suckled by F. The babies were transferred after they had absorbed at least some colostrum from their mothers, and probably too late to obtain any from their foster-mothers. F suckled by J showed no increased growth, but incorporated methionine rather more quickly than when suckled by F. The hybrids between the two strains at first resembled their mothers in methionine replacement, but when adult resembled strain F. The back cross to strain J showed some evidence of segregation for methionine synthesis. So far as I can interpret the translations of the statements of Shaumyan and Yudin (1949) it would seem that Soviet workers have found considerable maternal effects on economically important characters in cattle and sheep. Unfortunately, their original data are not available to me, nor do I know whether they have compared the effects of milk with those of prenatal environment. This would seem to be an obvious step in applying the theories of Michurin to animals, even though Rutman's data give no reason to suppose that in this case characters induced by milk are handed on indefinitely. It will be of great interest to determine the nature of the substance in milk responsible for this effect. As the stocks differ in growth rate, it is likely to have a general effect on protein synthesis rather than a specific one on the incorporation of methionine.

I now pass to a consideration of the effects of "training" and similar processes in unicellular organisms. When a culture of bacteria is placed in a new medium, some kind of adaptation is often found after a number of cell generations. This may be due to training, to selection of mutants, or to both.

To my mind it has been demonstrated quite conclusively that training occurs in some cases, that is to say that an organism acquires a biochemical aptitude which it did not formerly possess, or that if it possessed it the rate at which the process is performed is increased several thousand times. This is not, in itself, surprising. Further, in a number of cases (see Monod and Cohn, 1952) it has been shown that it does so by producing a particular catalyst. There is nothing surprising in this. The cells of a digestive gland, for example, may be able to "rest" completely, producing none of their characteristic enzyme. Certainly, under stimulation, they can increase its rate of production several hundred-fold. In favourable cases the amount of catalyst produced can be directly measured.

Thus Ephrussi and Slonimsky (1950) found that when yeast is grown anaerobically certain cytochrome absorption bands are invisible, and the yeast cannot use molecular oxygen at any great rate. On exposure to air, even in the absence of growth, the spectrum of new cytochrome components visible after reduction appears, and the ability to use oxygen correspondingly increases. The change is completed in about ten hours. When an air-adapted yeast is made to live under anaerobic conditions the total amount of cytochrome in the culture does not change greatly. Consequently the amount per cell is approximately halved per cell division, and after ten divisions must be reduced to one-thousandth on an average. In fact the aerobic cytochromes are no longer detectable after ten hours. The oxygen uptake, if the yeast is suddenly exposed to air again, falls off correspondingly. The cytochrome behaves in a passive manner, like a vital stain. A geneticist must take cognizance of this process, as he must take cognizance, if he is concerned with the genetics of immunity, with the passive transfer of antibodies from mother to child by the placenta, the colostrum, or the milk; but he is not concerned with the biology of the process of synthesis of adaptive enzymes any more than with that of digestive enzymes or antibodies, except in so far as either of them is under genetic control, as they may be. Monod and Cohn (1952) give an excellent summary both of knowledge and conjectures on this problem. A geneticist would not consider that he was concerned with a specifically genetical problem even if the synthesis of cytochrome went on for some time after the stimulus of oxygen was removed, provided its rate of synthesis was roughly halved at each cell division. He would conjecture that molecules of a cytochrome synthesizing enzyme were passively transferred to one or other of the daughter cells.

If, however, in response to a stimulus, a substance is produced which was previously not detectable, and this process continues for many cell generations after the stimulus has ceased, a geneticist is certainly concerned. Let us take an example from the work of Beale (1952). A clone of *Paramecium aurelia* has characteristic antigens, against which a rabbit can be immunized; and the immune serum agglutinates the clone in question, but not other clones. By exposure to immune serum in sub-lethal concentration, or by change of temperature, a clone can be induced to cease producing its former antigen, and to produce a new one; and this character of producing the new antigen can be transmitted for a considerable number of cell generations. There is no question of a passive transfer of antigen produced as a result of a temporary stimulus. Beale found that the kind of antigen produced was under genic control. A given cell can only produce a few of the repertory of antigens available to the species, however it is treated; but a suitable stimulus will cause it to cease forming the antigen determined by the genes which it carries at one locus, and to make one determined by the genes at a different locus.

It is possible that the antigen, once formed, gets itself copied with the aid of the gene whose presence in the nucleus is a necessary but not sufficient condition for its formation. This is not very probable, since most, if not all, of the antigen molecules are in the cell membrane. We may suppose that the metabolic processes concerned have been switched into a new path, and that this is a self-conserving dynamical pattern. The analogy with a self-conserving mode of vibration in a mechanical system is obvious, but may be misleading. Or we may suppose that one or more extra-nuclear self-reproducing systems, like those described earlier in this chapter, have been formed. As the genes can come into action again when the cell is suitably stimulated, there is not the faintest reason to think that they have been altered.

The important question for a geneticist, then, is not "Can a cell acquire a new function, and how long does it take to 'train' it?" but "How quickly is the training lost or 'forgotten'?" or "How quickly does reversion occur?" Unfortunately, in the large majority of cases described in the literature this question is not answered, and we do not know whether we are dealing with the passive transfer of an adaptive enzyme, or with the formation of a self-reproducing system. I know of no case in Neurospora where this has been decided conclusively. Many of its mutants, after a lag usually of the order of two or three days, will begin to grow at a fairly normal rate. Such a capacity is invariably lost on sexual reproduction, or reproduction by microconidia, which produce spores with little cytoplasm. This proves that the genes have not been altered. It does not enable us to decide whether the cytoplasmic components lost are merely enzyme molecules or a self-reproducing "mechanism" for making them. This could, perhaps, be decided by growing mycelia containing adaptive enzymes on a substrate where they are no longer required.

However, Hinshelwood and his colleagues have carried out experiments where passive transfer of adaptive enzymes cannot explain the facts. For example, Hinshelwood and Jackson (1950) adapted *Bacterium lactis aerogenes* to D-arabinose. After cultures of unadapted bacteria had been grown on various media, growth on arabinose was delayed for a time varying from 19 to 38 hours, and averaging about 30. The lag on glucose varied from 0 to 3 hours. The lag was shown not to be due to selection of mutants, for the lag was just the same when a culture was made from a single cell as when it was made from a large number, which would have contained some mutants, so that growth could have started at once. In cases where mutation occurs, the production of mutants in cultures derived from one or a very few cells is found to be extremely irregular. On reculturing adapted bacteria in glucose, the lag on retransferring to arabinose rose from 1 or 2 hours to 5 to 8 hours after 20 sub-cultures in glucose, but no further after 50. If reverse mutations had occurred it would have risen fairly steadily to the initial 30 hours. In each sub-culture the bacteria multiplied 100 to 1,000 times, so in some cases the increase was over 10^{100}. The possibility of passive dilution is absolutely excluded. On the other hand, Spiegelman and his colleagues (1950, 1951) worked with a yeast *Saccharomyces chevalieri*, which adapts to ferment galactose in the course of several days. During adaptation some individual cells are not adapted, while others are so. During reversion, or "forgetting," on a medium not containing galactose, the characters of individual cells are again sharply different, and after 7 or 8 cell generations most of the descendants of an adapted cell have lost their adaptation. This suggests that each cell contains about 100 molecules of "galactozymase," or of some system forming it, which are shared out when a cell divides, but only reproduce in presence of galactose.

Before discussing this question further, I shall briefly discuss the genetics of adaptation. Various bacteria, including *Escherichia coli*, either contain a β-galactosidase, can be trained to form it, or can mutate so as to be susceptible to such training. Cohn and Torriani (1951) (see also Monod and Cohn, 1952) found that they all contain an antigen Pz, possibly an enzyme, but not a β-galactosidase. When β-galactosidase is formed by training, the amount of Pz is about halved. It may be a precursor of β-galactosidase, but perhaps more probably both have a common precursor. In *E. coli* the capacity to form β-galactosidase can be lost and regained by mutation, spontaneous or provoked by ultraviolet radiation (Monod, 1949, 1950). Capacity to form amylomaltase, which reversibly converts half the glucose residues of maltose into starch:

$$n \text{ 4-glucosido-glucose} \rightleftharpoons n \text{ glucose} + (\text{glucose})_n$$
$$[\text{cf. } n \text{ glucose-1-phosphate} \rightleftharpoons n \text{ phosphate} + (\text{glucose})_n].$$

is determined in the same manner, presumably by another gene, but the evidence for genes in bacteria is, as we saw, less clear than in higher organisms.

On the other hand, Winge and Roberts (1948, 1952) have analysed the behaviour of yeasts genetically. Their later work is summarized on pp. 46–47. In their earlier research they found that *Saccharomyces cerevisiae* ferments maltose without adaptation, and galactose after adaptation, reaching half the maximum rate of galactose fermentation in eight days. On crossing with *S. chevalieri* the asci gives rise to a variety of haploid forms. The difference in adaptability to galactose seems to depend on one gene pair; but at least three other gene pairs are probably concerned in maltose fermentation. Some of the segregants can ferment it at once, some after a few hours, others after some days, and others again not at all.

Lindegren (1945) and Spiegelman, Lindegren and Lindegren (1945) (cf. also Spiegelman, 1946) crossed *Saccharomyces carlsbergensis* which can ferment melibiose (6, α-galactopyranosidoglucopyranose) after adaptation, with *S. cerevisiae* which cannot. The initial results were not clear, but suggested that several genes were segregating; however, further back-crosses gave single gene segregation. If conjugation, segregation, and the growth of a new haploid generation occurred in the absence of melibiose, the progeny of half the spores could be trained to ferment melibiose, that of the other half could not. If, however, these processes occurred in presence of melibiose, all the progeny could ferment it, even after over a thousand generations. When the cultures were kept in the absence of melibiose or a nitrogen source, so that hardly any cells divided, they lost their capacity to ferment melibiose in three weeks at most. Half could regain it on training, half could not. It seems, then, that the gene for adaptability to melibiose took part, in the presence of melibiose, in producing something which can reproduce itself, but only in presence of melibiose, after the gene has been lost by segregation. This something could be the enzyme or a "cytogene" producing it; the word "plasmagene" has also been used. I should prefer to keep such words to denote genetically stabler units, and to resurrect Coutagne's (1902) words "mnemon" for such at present hypothetical cell components. Unfortunately, it has not been possible to repeat this remarkable experiment (Lindegren, 1949). It must, however, be remembered that a yeast stock, even if meticulously guarded from contamination, is under heavy natural selection, and may be expected to change in some years. If the claims made are valid,[*] they in no way contradict the generally accepted principles of genetics. Catcheside (1949) points out that there are undoubted cases in higher plants where a gene initiates a change in an extranuclear component which is then reproduced in the absence of the gene. Ideally, then, we should like to know in every case how long, if at all, the induced character reproduces itself:

(a) in the absence of the stimulus responsible for its origin;
(b) in the absence of one or more genes responsible for its origin;
(c) in the absence of both.

---

[*] Spiegelman and De Lorenzo (1952) have obtained essentially similar results for adaption to ferment galactose.

It is clear that the answers to these questions probably differ from one case to another.

It must not be supposed that all cases of biochemical adaptation are due to training of this type. They can be due to reverse mutations.

Ryan and Lederberg (1946), Ryan (1947), and Sheng and Ryan (1948) investigated a case of this sort in *Neurospora crassa*. A leucine-less mutant l_1 usually grows at a standardized rate on media containing little leucine, but when the concentration is low enough, exceptions are common. Thus on 50 ml. of a medium containing 10 mg/litre of leucine, seven cultures produced $17 \cdot 2$–$18 \cdot 0$. mg. of mycelium; three others produced $19 \cdot 0$, $20 \cdot 1$ and $44 \cdot 8$ mg. Genetical analysis by crossing to another l_1 strain showed that in these three the gene l_1 had mutated back to the normal allelomorph L_1. To estimate leucine by this method it is better to use a double mutant $l_1 l_2$, since double back mutations are extremely rare. It was further found that the frequency with which back mutations were found was much greater on media containing little leucine, as if the mutation were adaptive. The mutants start as heterokaryons; so artificial heterokaryons were made up in which the L_1 and l_1 nuclei differed in respect of other genes also, so that their numbers could be counted. It was shown that in presence of moderate amounts of leucine such as 15 mg/litre, though not on minimal media, l_1 nuclei multiply more quickly than L_1. The reason for this is not clear, but it accounts for the fallacious appearance of adaptive mutation. In other cases, for example resistance to sulphanilamide, both cytoplasmic adaptation and mutation have occurred in Neurospora.

Although the subject is, perhaps, not strictly germane to this book, I shall also very briefly describe the use of bacterial training to elucidate metabolic paths. If we have a metabolic path

$$A \to B \to C \to D \to E$$
$$\quad \alpha \quad \beta \quad \gamma \quad \delta$$

where the enzyme catalysing a process is written below the arrow, then an untrained organism may lack all these enzymes, and if supplied with A it will make them all, but if supplied with D it will only make δ, so that if, after training on D, it is supplied with A, then B will accumulate when α has been made and β has not; C will accumulate when α and β have been made but γ has not, and so on. By this procedure Stanier (*vide* Monod and Cohn, 1952) has worked out the process of degradation of tryptophan by Pseudomonas. The steps are:—

tryptophan $\rightarrow$ formylkynurenine $\rightarrow$ kynurenine $\rightarrow$ $\begin{cases} \text{alanine} \\ \text{o-aminobenzoic} \end{cases}$
acid $\rightarrow$ catechol $\rightarrow$ cis-muconic acid $\rightarrow$ β-keto-adipic acid.

A number of the enzymes concerned have been obtained in solution. It is highly probable that formylkynurenine will yet be obtained from a Neurospora or Drosophila mutant. It is also worth remarking that the presence of large quantities of kynureninase, which is a specific peptidase hydrolysing kynurenine (o-amino-benzoyl-alanine) in Neurospora would cause a partial or complete block to the formation of 3-hydroxykynurenine.

We can now consider the standpoint adopted by Hinshelwood, who has worked on adaptive changes in bacteria, and, to a less extent, in yeasts. This standpoint is clearly stated in his book (Hinshelwood, 1946). He believes that growth is explained by an autosynthesis of enzymes. He gives some examples of inorganic reactions where, in his own words (p. 16),

"Catalyst + substrate = more catalyst + product,"

and continues (p. 22): "Moreover, in a constant medium the various enzymes and other cell substances are formed in a constant ratio, so they *must* all obey the same law of autosynthesis. Thus an important equation of cell synthesis *must* be: enzyme + substrate = more enzyme + products (possibly utilizable for further synthesis)." (My italics.) This is, no doubt, a way in which, given our present knowledge, growth may occur, and perhaps sometimes does, but it seems rash to assume that it always does so. It does not happen *in vitro*. The only cases where enzymes make more of themselves *in vitro* is when an inactive precursor such as trypsinogen is present, and in this case more trypsin is made whether or not it is digesting another protein, in fact probably more slowly if it is doing so. Further, Monod, Cohen-Bazire and Cohn (1951) found that all the substances hydrolyzed by adaptive bacterial β-galactosidase induced its formation. However, phenyl-β-thiogalactoside, which is not hydrolyzed, but unites with the enzyme, inhibiting it competitively, does not do so. These results agree with Hinshelwood's theory, but not with that of Yudkin (1938). But melibiose (an α-galactoside) which is not hydrolyzed, and does not inhibit, is as efficient as lactose in inducing enzyme formation, and galactose is somewhat less efficient, though much more so than β-naphthylgalactoside, which is hydrolyzed. Clearly the inducing power depends on structure, but is independent of combination with the enzyme, let alone with being one of its substrates.

Numerous authors before Hinshelwood have stated in the past that a living organism must work in a certain way. Descartes thought that they worked like the simple machines which he knew, and to-day some neurologists, and perhaps more mathematicians, think that brains work like electronic computers. In fact, living organisms have turned out to be more complicated than was supposed. In higher animals regulation is often a roundabout affair depending on the conflict between antagonistic processes. For example, the internal secretions of the thyroid, adrenals, and gonads are promoted by hormones secreted by the anterior pituitary whose production is inhibited by the hormones produced by the other glands. The production of adaptive enzymes may be an equally complex process. I do not attempt to answer the question whether organisms will ultimately be describable as mechanisms. The answer may depend on the definition of the word "mechanism." This word is highly ambiguous, and anyone who supposes that it is emotionally un-charged would be well advised to read Kipling's *Macandrew's Hymn* and *The Derelict*, and to look at some of the paintings of Hieronymus Bosch.

Lysenko's (1949, p. 39) view, so far as I can follow it, seems to be essentially similar. "Consequently," he writes, "the plastic sub-stances produced by the scion and the stock possess the characters of the breed, are endowed with definite heredity just as the chromo-somes, and just as any particle of the living body." (It is only fair to Lysenko to assume that the Russian phrase translated as "plastic substances" has a more precise meaning. Nor is it clear whether "any" means "some" or "every.") In 1902 Correns, one of the re-discoverers of Mendel's work, and certainly a Mendelist, perhaps even a "Mendel-Morganist" as he postulated the linear arrangement of genes on chromosomes long before Morgan, demonstrated the existence in some plants of extra-nuclear units capable of self-propagation, or of being copied by the rest of the cell, and thus "endowed with definite heredity." These may be more important and more responsive to the environment than most biologists outside the Soviet Union think, but the fact that both in plants and animals reciprocal crosses generally, though not always, give indistinguish-able progeny, shows that they are less important than nuclear factors. But there is no evidence that every enzyme, let alone "any particle of the living body," is "endowed with definite heredity." There is conclusive evidence that many of them are not. If, for example, the atropine esterase of rabbits were so endowed, then all or almost all the progeny of a female rabbit possessing this enzyme would possess it too. In this case it is quite clear that a gene is "endowed with heredity," so far as a precise meaning can be attached to this phrase, and the enzyme is not.

Hinshelwood (especially Dean and Hinshelwood, 1952) has produced extremely strong evidence that adaptive enzyme formation by bacteria is sometimes direct, and not due to selection of mutants. Perhaps such evidence was needed in view of the dogmatism of a small minority of geneticists to the contrary. He has also thrown doubt on some of the arguments used to support the hypothesis of mutation in bacteria. Kilkenny and Hinshelwood (1952) have further shown that the times needed for several types of training were different in the progeny of different spores from the same diploid yeast culture. Their comments on this fact show a curious attitude to genetics. Referring to thirteen spores, of which one gave cultures flocculating in such a way as to prevent measurement, they write: "It is interesting to note that at first sight these seemed to fall into two groups as if there had been Mendelian segregation." In fact, five spores showed no lag in adapting to galactose, five had lag periods from 260 to 610 minutes, and two had lags of 2,150 and 3,000 minutes. Even if I were breeding elephants, where large numbers are unattainable, I should hesitate to postulate Mendelian segregation on such data. Mendelian segregation can hardly ever be deduced from data on less than three generations.

The views of these authors are more clearly expressed in an earlier paper (Kilkenny and Hinshelwood, 1951). "In its origin," they write, "the gene was a hypothetical entity whose presence or absence, calculated according to the theory of probability, explained the qualitative occurrence or non-occurrence of certain characters in an organism, and the existence of simple ratios in inheritance." This is not the case. For example, Mendel worked with tall and short pea plants. The difference is quantitative, and a starved pea plant with the genes for tallness can be shorter than a well-grown plant with those for shortness. Whatever part the theory of probability may have played in early genetics, modern fungal genetics are based on exact or almost exact equality of two classes. Chemical atoms, like genes, were once hypothetical entities, but Hinshelwood has seen individual helium atoms in a spinthariscope, and I have seen such genes as Bar and Notch in Drosophila. The authors go on to describe the opinions of certain geneticists who postulate "polygenes" and "modifiers" to account for more or less continuous variation, and criticize them with considerable justice. They would find equally strong criticisms of "polygenes" in recent genetical literature; but it

G

is quite incorrect to suppose that a character determined by a gene "should be absolutely present or absolutely absent." Since the technique for doing so has been standardized, no one has had any difficulty in classifying a phenylketonuric; nevertheless, it is possible that even Hinshelwood excretes a milligram of phenylalanine per day.

A biochemical geneticist may hope that a particular molecular species, say a particular enzyme, is completely absent from a certain genotype; but in practice he usually estimates crystalloids such as sugars or pigments, which may or may not be completely absent, and if he gets clear segregation in the expected ratios along with qualitative evidence of Mendelian inheritance, he postulates a pair of genes.

And some cases of apparently continuous inheritance have been analysed in terms of a finite number of genes. Thus de Winton and Haldane (1933) showed that the apparently continuous variation of the anthocyanin content of the stems and leaves of *Primula sinensis* was mainly determined by three gene pairs, one incompletely dominant. These gave twelve phenotypes, some of which overlapped a little; but as two of these genes affected the petal colour in quite a characteristic way, there was rarely any doubt about the genetical formula of a given plant, unless a gene suppressing pigmentation in the petals was present. Three other genes which affected flower colour considerably had slight effects on stem colour, as did the environment. The analysis was tedious but not difficult. It was undertaken precisely because we regarded the situation as a challenge.

A student of higher plants and animals, therefore, finds no reason to agree with Kilkenny and Hinshelwood's conclusion that "the rigidly localized gene is likely to be a limiting case, and the purely Mendelian type of segregation to be rather rare," or with the more dogmatic and more minatory pronouncements of Lysenko to the same effect. The cells in a higher animal no doubt undergo changes like those in adapting yeast cells (Knox and Mehler, 1950). Some of these changes may possibly induce changes in the offspring, through the milk or otherwise; but, as we have seen, there is evidence particularly from the effects of sporulation in Neurospora, that these biochemical adaptations are wholly extra-nuclear, and it is at least plausible that the genes are desoxyribonucleoproteins, the self-reproducing cytoplasmic units being more usually ribonucleoproteins. Organic chemistry, unlike silicate chemistry, is a field in which there is no room for continuous variation.

It is entirely possible that in bacteria the cellular organization is so primitive that distinctions which are sharp in other groups can no longer be made; but in all higher organisms I think that the notion of the gene as a limiting case is a step backwards. Because Paramecium has no definite mouth we are not justified in saying that vertebrates do not have one. It is unfortunate that Hinshelwood has only worked with bacteria, whose genetics are almost unknown, and with yeasts, where they are highly controversial. I venture to hope that he may yet work with such an organism as Neurospora or Aspergillus, whose genetics are well established, and in which adaptation is known to occur. Either a complete disentanglement of the effects of training from those of genes, or a proof that training can alter genes, would be of the greatest importance to biology.

It is only fair to add that some workers, particularly in America, while probably not denying the existence of adaptive enzymes, appear to deny that their synthesis continues, or is in any way facilitated, when the stimulus to it ceases. It is reasonable to adopt this view as a working hypothesis during a critical examination of such results as those of Hinshelwood, but to adopt it without further ado to explain such results is, in my opinion, a piece of dogmatism as regrettable as that of Lysenko in the opposite direction.

CHAPTER VIII

Mutation, and the Problem of Gene Reproduction

The word mutation is not strictly defined, because we cannot, in general, distinguish between changes due to the loss or duplication of a small portion of a chromosome, a change in the order of the genes in a chromosome, and a so-called "point mutation," better a molecular mutation, affecting a single gene. This is, however, often possible in Diptera such as Drosophila which have giant chromosomes up to $0 \cdot 5$ mm long in some of their cells, and refined cytological technique is beginning to make it possible in maize, mice, and newts. The matter is further complicated because many agents produce both types of mutation.

Spontaneous mutations occur. For example, if a normal-eyed, normal-winged stock of *Drosophila melanogaster* is kept, with paired matings in each generation, white-eyed males and notch-winged females will turn up. The white-eyed mutation is due to a change in a very small region of the X chromosome, of which females have two and males only one. It is recessive in females, but shows up in males which have only one gene at this locus. *Notch* is due to the loss of a small but visible section of chromosome usually, but not always, including the locus of white. It has a slight effect on the wing tips of heterozygous females, and is lethal to males. That is to say, one or more of the genes in this section is essential to life, but when only one instead of two is present, the only effect is a slight failure of wing growth. In each of these cases the mutation rate can be estimated, which is much harder in the case of autosomal recessives. The frequency with which each of these mutations occurs per chromosome per generation is of the order of 10^{-6}. Other less drastic mutations occur at the locus of white, giving various pink and yellowish eye colours. The total frequency of such detectable mutations is less than that of mutations to white, completely suppressing pigment formation.

Let us see what this means biochemically. A Drosophila contains about 2^{25} cells. A representative cell is thus derived from the fertilized egg by 25 mitoses. The number may, perhaps, be a little less for early eggs, a little more for late spermatozoa. If, then, we assume that the gene for normal eye colour is a molecule which is copied at each nuclear division, the given mutation rate means that the copying goes wrong about once in twenty-five million times, an impressively large number. Nevertheless, a recessive lethal appears somewhere in an X chromosome about once in 1,000 life cycles, and in the other chromosomes with a comparable frequency. If the mutation rate per gene per life cycle were one per 1,000, most animals would die of lethal genes, since many, perhaps most, mutations are lethal, and a higher animal contains several thousand loci. When a mutation occurs one of three things may have happened. The copying process itself may have failed. Or, in between two copying processes, the gene may have been altered in one of two ways. It may have been altered into a copiable form, or it may have been altered into a form which could not be exactly copied with the available enzymes and raw materials, the copy made being the best possible.

Such spontaneous mutation in Drosophila has a Q_{10} of about 5. Since mutagenesis by X-rays has no temperature coefficient it is clear that natural radioactivity and cosmic rays can account for only a small fraction of natural mutation. A few abnormal genes have very high mutation rates. Flaked flowers are due to a recessive white gene (often allelomorphic with a stable recessive or dominant white) which is constantly mutating back to normal, so that anything from perhaps 2% to 0·1% of the seeds from such a plant give fully coloured flowers. The flakes are due to mutations back to normal during somatic growth. Schrödinger (1944) on the basis of a rather simple theory, suggested that this process should have a high temperature coefficient. In fact Fabergé and Beale (1942) had found that in one case it had a negative one. Spontaneous mutation in man is probably rather more frequent per locus per generation than in Drosophila (Haldane, 1948).

Muller (1928) found that mutation rates could be increased 100 to 200 times by X-rays. They are also induced by γ-rays, ultra-violet radiation of germ-cells, and by α- and β-particles. As a result of quantitative work on this effect the size of genes was calculated. For an excellent summary see Lea (1946). From two quite different arguments Lea concluded that genes had diameters from 20–60 Å, and from 40–90 Å, giving reasons for supposing the lower range to be an underestimate. Haldane (1920), on very inadequate grounds, had estimated the minimum distance between two genes in a chromosome as 20 Å. This is perhaps the earliest estimate of a gene size.

Now Lea's estimates, and others based on similar work, are open to a formidable criticism which we shall shortly consider; but he applied the same method to estimate the molecular weight of one enzyme and four viruses whose molecular weight had been determined by other methods. The molecular weights found varied from 2·1 to 0·22 times those found by other methods. In the worst case the diameter calculated was 0·6 of what is thought to be the true diameter. Any criticism of the method as applied to genes is equally valid against its application to viruses. It is, therefore, probable that genes have molecular weights of the order of a million. The number of single gene mutations produced is closely proportional to the total dose of radiation. The number of rearrangements, which depend on double chromosome breaks, goes up more nearly with the square of the dose. Ultra-violet radiation usually produces single gene mutations only.

The fact that the frequency of gene mutations is proportional to the dose of radiation and independent of its intensity proves that a single process, whether biochemical or biophysical, alters a gene. This would not be the case if a gene were composed of several like parts. If, for example, two hits by high-speed particles, or two oxidations by a peroxide, were needed to inactivate a gene, the rate of production of lethal mutations would rise as the square of the dose. In fact it rises rather more rapidly than the dose, but this is because many lethal mutations are due to double chromosome breaks causing the loss of sections. When these are detected by special methods the proportionality of the remainder to the dose is pretty exact. The attempt to estimate gene numbers is more doubtful, being subject to the same criticisms as the estimates of gene size. Lea estimated the number of genes in the X chromosome of Drosophila as 840–280, the total number in a nucleus being 5–10 times larger, in *E. coli* 250, vaccinia virus 110, in bacteriophage 14. If, however, the gene size is not uniform, these numbers are too low. Estimates for bacteriophage on other grounds range up to 100.

A beautiful edifice of speculation was reared on the mutagenic effect of radiations and particles. A highly poetical version of it may be found in Schrödinger (1944). It was brought down to earth by three fundamental observations. Auerbach and Robson (1942, 1947) were allowed to publish their finding that β–β'-dichlorethyl sulphide causes large numbers of mutations in Drosophila.* Earlier claims

---

* Publication was delayed, apparently because some official believed that this news would spread panic. Had he remained in London during its aerial bombardments he might have taken a view more complimentary to the British people.

for chemical mutagens are of doubtful validity. Thoday and Read (1948) found that the number of chromosomal breaks produced by irradiation of Tradescantia pollen increases with the partial pressure of oxygen, the number produced in nitrogen being about a quarter of that in air. Stone, Wyss and Haas (1947) showed that the irradiation of a medium on which bacteria are later grown will produce mutations like those caused by directly irradiating the bacteria.

It became clear that mutagenesis is a biochemical rather than a biophysical process. Some of the effect of radiations and high-speed particles may be due to direct hits on chromosomal organic substance. Most of it is due to the formation of mutagenic substances. Radiation and high-speed particles are efficient because they can generate such substances inside the nucleus, whereas if they are injected or given in the food they have to pass through a number of membranes and through living substance which destroys them to a large extent. It is, nevertheless, far from clear how in detail the partial pressure of oxygen influences mutagenesis by X- or γ-radiation. As one example of the highly intriguing evidence on this question I mention the work of King, Schneiderman and Sax (1952). They irradiated *Tradescantia paludosa* pollen grains with 400 r of X-rays, and counted the number in which chromosomal rearrangements had been produced. They found that pollen exposed during radiation to 1 atmosphere's pressure of air + 5 atmospheres O_2 gave $8 \cdot 4$–$9 \cdot 5\%$ of cells with rearrangements, 1 atmosphere of air + 5 atmospheres of CO gave $14 \cdot 8$–$16 \cdot 1\%$, provided the grains had been exposed for an hour or more to the CO before irradiation began. They suggested that the CO inhibited cytochrome oxidase, and that flavoprotein enzymes were unusually active, making peroxide, which was then "activated" by the radiation. But Mefferd and Matney (1952) report that CO protects *Escherichia coli* from the effects of ultra-violet radiation in presence of O_2, though it has no effect in the absence of O_2, which considerably reduces the effect of radiation.

The whole question has been complicated by Conger and Fairchild's (1952) announcement that oxygen at atmospheric pressure, or compressed air containing the same partial pressure of oxygen, will induce rearrangements in Tradescantia pollen. Pure O_2 for one hour at atmospheric pressure has the effect of 1,200 r of X-rays, 65% O_2 that of 350 r. This result contradicts some earlier work, and until it has been confirmed it would, perhaps, be ill advised to argue from it.

I have no intention of summarizing the large amount of data which have been published on mutagenic substances. I do not include radioactive elements, which naturally act in the same way as particles or radiation of high energy. Radiophosphorus, which is, of course, incorporated into the nucleus in large amounts, is particularly efficient. The simplest known ones include formaldehyde (Rappoport, 1946) and nitrous acid (Rendel, personal communication) added to the food. The obvious explanation of their action is that they affect the amino groups of proteins and thus derange protein synthesis in nuclei. But $MnCl_2$ appears to be a mutagen for some bacteria. (Demerec, 1953)

Among the more efficient mutagenic substances are epoxides such as 1 : 2, 3 : 4-diepoxy-butane (Bird, 1952), sulphur and nitrogen "mustards." Even caffeine (Fries and Kihlmann, 1948) appears to have such an effect on one fungus. It might be expected to interfere with nucleic acid synthesis. A number of carcinogenic substances, such as dibenzanthracene, are also mutagenic. Reviews are given by Auerbach (1949), Carr (1950) and Demerec (1949). Haddow (1949) suggested that a number of these compounds may act by linking up protein or nucleic acid chain molecules, and thus producing abnormal patterns of a type which can be copied. Finally Emerson (1944) immunized rabbits to Neurospora and treated conidia with the antisera. A number of variants were isolated, many of which were single gene mutants. One gene mutated very frequently. Unfortunately this work, which promises the possibility of inducing specific mutations, has not been followed up. Such a process could explain some cases of loss by "disuse." A tissue, particularly one isolated from the circulation, such as the lens, could immunize the rest of the body against itself if it were so damaged that antigens from it passed into the blood. If the genes responsible for the production of these antigens are attacked by the same antibodies, mutation could occur. There is some evidence that this may take place. It is hardly necessary to emphasize the interest of following up this work with serum containing antibodies against a purified enzyme or antigen. Such antibodies cause antigenic change, but so far *not* mutation, in Paramecium.

On the whole the effects of these mutagens are non-specific. Nevertheless, there are considerable statistical differences between them. Thus mustard gas produces mutations after a much greater delay than radiation, and may then produce a number of similar mutants, as if it had made copying difficult but not impossible. A much greater specificity is shown by mutagenic genes, for example in maize (Rhoades, 1949) the gene Dt induces mutations in the gene *a* concerned in anthocyanin synthesis, and so far as is known in no others.

One point must be made clear. Mutation is sometimes dismissed or at least decried as "injury" or "damage." It is obvious that if an organism is well adapted to its environment most mutations will lessen its efficiency in that environment, though they may help it in another one (e.g. a mutant barley produced in southern Sweden which was a conspicuous success on the Arctic Circle). It is also easier to lose an old function than to gain a new one. A recessive gene *can* be a structural loss, but it need not be so, because X-rays can provoke mutation of dominant to recessive and then of recessive back to dominant. Both cannot be "damage." A recessive gene which can mutate back to perform its normal function must have been reproducing itself, though in an "inactive" form, in the meantime. A mutant gene which is inactive, and has never been known to mutate back, may be completely abolished, and sometimes at least is so. Further, mutation is certainly part of the evolutionary process; for some of the differences between related species can be shown to be due to genes, and almost all of them may be.

The modern Soviet school, in so far as they believe in anything corresponding to genes, appear to think that mutation is often adaptive, a nuclear organ increasing or decreasing in activity with use, this change being handed on. They rightly point out that the chromosomes take part in metabolic processes, and arise by them. The question how far they are altered in consequence is a question of fact. The evidence seems to be against the view that such adaptive changes are at all common. This may be simply because genes do not generally play a very direct part in metabolic processes, and we do not know how to influence them.

Apart from mutagenesis, irreversible changes of a different character may be produced in a nucleus, the most striking and stable being the induction of polyploidy. This can be brought about in many plants by colchicine. Schmuck (1938) tested a large number of other compounds, of which the most successful was acenaphthene. Östergren and Levan (1943) continued the work on a large scale. Interesting as their results are, they probably throw more light on the mechanism of mitosis than on that of genic reproduction.

Chromosomes normally consist of desoxyribonucleic acid (DNA) combined more or less firmly with a protein which may, according to circumstances, be anything from a "whole" protein to a protamine. It is possible that ribonucleic acid is sometimes found in some parts of certain chromosomes, and it is possible that all chromosomes, at some stage in their cycle, may consist wholly or mainly of protein. Some certainly do so.

The amount of DNA in a nucleus can be measured by optical and chemical methods, which agree provided the amount per nucleus is uniform, as is the case in most tissues. Boivin, Vendrely and Tulasne (1949) and Vendrely (1950) give some figures, and Leuchtenberger, Vendrely and Vendrely (1951) compare optical and chemical methods and discuss discrepancies in earlier data.

The amount of DNA in a mammalian nucleus is usually about $6 \cdot 5$ to $5 \cdot 0 \times 10^{-6} \mu g$, except in spermatozoa where it is half this quantity, and in the livers of some (but not all) species where tetraploid and even octoploid cells are found. In most birds and fish the somatic nuclear content is $1 \cdot 7$ to $2 \cdot 2 \times 10^{-6} \mu g$, though some (probably polyploid) teleosts approach the mammalian figure. In one echinoderm it is about the same. The bacterial nucleus, which can be seen after removing the ribonucleic acid with ribonuclease, contains about $10^{-8} \mu g$, roughly one-three-hundredth of a mammalian haploid nucleus. The molecular weights of the four types of nucleotide residue in a chain are 318, 302, 293 and 278, with a mean of 298. This means that a mammalian nucleus contains $1 \cdot 3 \times 10^{10}$ nucleotide residues, a bacterial nucleus 2×10^7 residues. If they were all arranged in one chain this implies that if there are equal numbers n of the four types of nucleotide, which is nearly, though not quite, true, they could be arranged in $\dfrac{(4n!)}{(n!)^4}$, or nearly $2^{8n+1}(2n\pi)^{-\frac{3}{2}}$ ways. This is somewhat under 2^{8n} or $2^{4 \times 10^7}$. Thus if all the different arrangements were possible, and controlled metabolism in a different way, a bacterial nucleus would convey about 4×10^7 units of control, measured as binary choices like turning left or right. Chambers's logarithm tables (omitting the 8-figure part) convey just over 2×10^6 units. To put the matter rather differently, a Ph.D. candidate who was asked to make one molecule of each of all the desoxyribonucleic acids containing 27 residues each of the four nucleotides, would require a mass of raw material about 10^{11} times that of the sun, and approximately equal to that of our galaxy. Whereas a bacterial nucleus contains not 27, but about five million, of each of these types.

In fact there is no reason to think that much of the nuclear DNA is specific in the sense that its pattern exercises metabolic control. The number of genes in a nucleus can be calculated from the minimal doses of various kinds of radiation which kill different types of cell (Lea, 1946). This varies from about 110 for vaccinia, and 250 for *E. coli*, to about 4,000 for a Drosophila cell. These figures are, perhaps, too low if some genes are very resistant, but the number for Drosophila is confirmed on quite different grounds. Even if a mammalian cell contains 40,000 genes, which is an improbably high figure, and the mean molecular weight is a million, the total is only 4×10^{10} Daltons, or 1% of the nucleic acid in the chromosomes. The genes thus form a small fraction of the total, and there is no conclusive evidence that they consist in whole or part of DNA. The main arguments for this hypothesis are as follows (see also Vendrely, 1950):

1. Changes produced in the chromosomal structure by X-rays and other means, for example reciprocal translocations, in which chromosomes A and B interchange segments, are faithfully copied at very large numbers of nuclear divisions. So are changes in genes, as deduced from their effects on the whole organism.

2. Bacterial transforming principles consist of fairly pure DNA, and are not destroyed by enzymes which attack other kinds of macromolecule.

3. Some viruses consist of DNA nucleoprotein, but others are RNA nucleoprotein, or mixed.

We do not know the nature of the differences between genes which determine their different activities. The unit differences may be very much larger than the substitution of one base for another in DNA, and probably are so.

There has been an immense amount of speculation as to the method by which chromosomes and genes are reproduced. A good many, but by no means all, of the theories are referred to by Muller (1947). My hypothesis is a development of that of Friedrich–Freksa (1940). The fundamental fact to be explained is as follows. When a cell has been altered most of the alterations are reversible. Some are irreversible, or only reversible by the relatively infrequent process of mutation. Most of these copiable changes occur in the nucleus and can be located by genetical methods. A certain amount of copying goes on outside the nucleus, e.g. in the case of the antigens described in Chapter VII, p. 90, but only rarely (cf. Chapter VII) is the copying as "stable" as nuclear copying. A living cell must contain "mechanisms" which will copy any of a very large number of models with very great fidelity, and others (multimutating genes) with moderate fidelity.

The two simplest hypotheses as to the copying process are as follows:

1. The model is spread out in a one-dimensional chain or a two-dimensional sheet, consisting of standard residues, nucleotides, amino-acids, and perhaps other prosthetic groups. The copiable units in a pattern may, of course, be peptides, polynucleotides, and

so on. On this chain or sheet another precisely similar chain or sheet is laid down by a process analogous to crystallization, the constituent groups being linked together by enzymes, perhaps like those which are known to be concerned in polysaccharide synthesis. We now have two sub-hypotheses:

1(a). This process takes place throughout the nuclear cycle. Most of the copies float off, and are primary gene products, chemically similar to the gene. Only once in a nuclear cycle is a whole chromosome copied, the gene copies adhering to it.

1(b). The copying process only occurs once in a nuclear cycle. The metabolic activities of genes are essentially catalytic; and we may regard the free nucleotides such as ATP and the co-enzymes, and protein-bound nucleotides such as the diaphorases, as models for the metabolic activity of genes.

2. The genes and the whole chromosome are "copied" into a completely different structure, the relation being, perhaps, like that of antigen and antibody. This "template" or "negative" is again copied, giving *two* new positives. We may symbolize this process as $C \rightarrow C' \rightarrow C_1 + C_2$. A further speculation is that C consists of nucleic acid, C' of protein, or conversely. The close agreement of the distances between neighbouring units in protein and nucleic acid chain molecules renders this speculation attractive. If so every gene is scrapped at every nuclear division.

It has long been known that some fish spermatozoan nuclei consist of a compound of nucleic acid with very simple basic proteins largely composed of arginine, while normal cell nuclei contain complex proteins. It is more probable that the specificity is embodied in the nucleic acid than in the protamines. Tomlin and Callan (1951) have recently isolated chromosomes from amphibian oocyte nuclei, and find that they are, at the diplotene stage, protein threads with little or no nucleic acid.

Any account of the copying process must explain what happens in meiosis as well as at mitosis. In meiosis two homologous parental chromosomes come to lie side by side in the zygotene stage. There is strong reason to think that homologous sections of the chromosomes are in exact contact. A like to like attraction of this kind is a general property of chromosomes. Its mechanism is by no means obvious since the chromosomes are built of asymmetrical residues. Two like segments can pair at this stage. If there are three like segments, one is left out. The paired chromosomes then coil up in the pachytene stage, and detailed observation is often difficult. When next visible, in early diplotene, each can be seen to be double, consisting of two chromatids. These paired chromatids are associated at a finite number of points called chiasmata. Combined genetical and cytological analyses (cf. Darlington, 1937) has made it clear that the chromatids lying together are derived from the same parental chromosome, but that at each chiasma one of them undergoes "crossing-over" with a chromatid derived from another parent. It is also clear, particularly from genetical observations on asco-mycetes, that all four chromatids can take part in such exchanges. The later stages of meiosis are simply the unravelling of this tangle, and may give rise to four spores or spermatozoa, each containing one chromosome from a set of four homologues, and each containing maternal and paternal segments.

The copying process presumably occurs at pachytene. On hypo-thesis (1) it would be expected that one pair of chromatids, the models, would be intact, the other pair, the copies, consisting both of maternal and paternal portions. On hypothesis (2) both pairs are copies, and it is intelligible that each should be a mixed copy of maternal and paternal material. If this is correct, crossing over, in the sense of chromosome breakage and subsequent reunion, never occurs.

To return to Tomlin and Callan's observations: the large diplotene chromosomes of Triturus oocytes are protein threads about 200 Å in diameter, apparently Feulgen-negative and therefore containing little or no DNA, and showing no sign of doubleness under the electron microscope. If we assume that along each of them two threads of nucleic acid are laid down, but at a junction such threads sometimes exchange partners, we have the necessary conditions for "crossing over" (cf. Fig. 7). A possible reason why just two copies are

FIG. 7

A cross-over. This may always occur at junctions if the nucleic acid threads are formed on opposite sides of a protein ribbon, and the threads whose course is interrupted by the junction always cross over.

No cross-over. This situation may never occur at a junction.

formed is that one nucleic acid ribbon is laid down on each side of a protein ribbon. This would, however, be easier to imagine were these ribbons built of symmetrical residues.

An argument against this hypothesis is that chromosomes can be broken by X-rays (or more probably products of absorption of X-rays) and can then rejoin, not always at the points where they were originally broken. Another adverse argument is that crossing over can occur at mitosis in a diploid. This is a rare event in Drosophila, but quite common in *Aspergillus niger* (Pontecorvo *et al.*, 1952). It is, however, quite possible that homologous chromosomes may occasionally come into contact of the same type as at zygotene. Again, the like to like attraction of chromosomes, and probably genes, at zygotene is more readily reconciled with hypothesis (1) than (2). Nevertheless, I am inclined to prefer hypothesis (2) to hypothesis (1). The history of science, however, suggests that each may be found to have a measure of truth. For example, the nucleic acid C might cause the formation of a certain amount of C' protein during the resting stage.

Most geneticists believe in crossing over, that is to say breakage of two chromosomes at homologous points followed by exchange. This process has generally been thought of in mechanical terms. It is at least equally fruitful to think of it in chemical terms. Transpeptidization in peptide chains and transglycosidation in polysaccharide chains are already known. It is at least possible that similar changes can be induced in nucleic acid chains. We should, perhaps, have then to picture the process of crossing over as consisting, in so far as it affected proteins, of a series of simultaneous transpeptidizations.

CHAPTER IX

Tentative Conclusions

Let us try to summarize our conclusions. Genetical analysis has led to a quasi-atomic theory. Heredity depends to a large extent on units called genes. If the very tentative conclusion of the last chapter is correct, a gene is the name which, at any moment, we give to a part of a chromosome with a specific function. But so far from genes being "immortal," which Lysenko (1949) asserts to be an essential tenet of "Mendel-Morganism," they are destroyed at every nuclear division, while other cell constituents may enjoy a considerably longer life. If hypothesis (2) of the last chapter is correct, the "same" gene can be represented in nucleic acid or in protein, as the "same" film can be represented in positive or negative. Probably during most of a cell's life, when the genes are metabolically functional, a given gene consists of nucleoprotein. But the gene as a chemically definable object existing in a given cell at a given moment is a product of metabolism like any other cellular constituent. To what extent genes are altered as a result of changed metabolic processes is a question of fact, and not of principle. My own opinion is that they are surprisingly stable in this respect.

It is concluded that in every cell there are one or two molecules (or molecular groupings if a chromosome is a giant molecule) which perform a function qualitatively different from any other molecules in the cell, and that this is so for thousands of different functions. The same conclusion has been reached from several other lines of argument. McIlwain (1946) gives the numbers of molecules of eight B vitamins per cell of seven bacterial species and their rates of synthesis during normal growth. The numbers per cell are mostly between 1,000 and 10,000, the rates of synthesis may be well under 1 per second, and only in the case of nicotinic acid and pantothenic acid do they exceed 10 per second. The velocities, in molecules per cell per second, of directly observed rates of destruction and more rarely synthesis of these compounds ranged from 5 to 540. The latter was, however, the rate of synthesis of pantothenic acid in presence of added β-alanine, which is normally a limiting factor. Now the rates of turnover in enzymatic reactions *in vitro* range from 14 to 44,000 substrate molecules per enzyme molecule per second. The median value for 16 enzymes is 300.* These enzymes were, however, working at optimal substrate concentrations and under otherwise optimal conditions.

McIlwain concluded that the number of catalyst molecules per cell concerned in the synthesis and breakdown of such substances is of the order of unity. It is clear, on the other hand, that a bacterial cell contains several thousand molecules of a number of enzymes concerned in "primary" metabolic processes, for example carboxylase or cytochrome oxidase. These numbers are of the same order as those of the vitamins which are sometimes incorporated in their coenzymes or prosthetic groups. McIlwain points out that if the genes are not the direct catalysts in such processes as vitamin synthesis, they can produce only a very few enzyme molecules in their lifetime "and introduce the necessity of coupling accurately with cell division two processes concerning individual molecules, the formation both of one gene and the associated enzyme." There is good reason to suggest that the genes are direct catalysts. A gene which produced 50 coenzyme molecules per second each of which could catalyse a change in 50 molecules of glucose per second, would thus control the metabolism, during a generation of 20 minutes, of 2×10^9 glucose molecules, or more than the mass of the bacterium.

These figures are, perhaps, applicable to yeasts and fungal spores, but McIlwain points out that they are probably not applicable to large cells such as Amoeba or Paramecium. It is not so clear whether they are applicable to cells or hyphae of metazoa, fungi and higher plants. In particular Wagner (1949) has isolated an enzyme synthesizing pantothenic acid from Neurospora. McIlwain describes catalysts responsible for a turnover of the order of 10^{-6} mol of substrate per mg. dry weight per hour as millimicromolar.

In *Lactobacillus arabinosus*, which requires exogenous nicotinic acid, McIlwain (1949) found that lactic acid is produced per molecule of nicotinic acid (which is mostly probably converted into cozymase) at a rate varying from 5 to 1 molecule per molecule per second, and that the nicotinic acid is used up after catalysing the formation of 500,000 to 800,000 molecules of lactic acid. If similar figures hold for organisms which can produce their own nicotinic acid, this would mean that one gene could supply the nicotinic acid needed to catalyse

* Baldwin's (1952, p. 208) list of 8 enzymes gives turnover numbers from 40,000 to 7, with a median about 80.

the metabolism of about 300,000 glucose molecules per second, or rather more than the figure reached in his earlier calculation.

Let us now consider another piece of evidence. The localization of genes in the chromosomes of Drosophila, Mus, or Zea has, on the face of it, no rhyme or reason. Genes controlling apparently very different developmental processes are often close together. However, fairly often two neighbouring genes have indistinguishable effects (e.g. *miniature* and *dusky*, *Star* and *asteroid* in *Drosophila melanogaster*). Pontecorvo (1952) and Pontecorvo *et al.* (1952) give other examples. Roper (1950) worked with three mutant strains of *Aspergillus nidulans* each requiring biotin, desthiobiotin, or 7-8-diamino-pelargonic acid, and not responding to pimelic acid. He found that the genes bi_1, bi_2 and bi_3 were all very closely linked, the frequencies of recombination not exceeding 1 per 1,000 gametes formed. The spatial distance between them is thus probably of the order of $\frac{1}{2000}$ of the chromosome length, which again is perhaps of the order of 100 μ* or 10^6 Å.* Thus the genes may be within a range of 500 Å or so; in fact they may be anchored to the chromosome so closely together that they can actually unite with the same biotin precursors, as an enzyme and its coenzyme can do in similar cases. A similar calculation for two still more closely linked genes in *A. nidulans* for p-aminobenzoic acid synthesis which recombine once in 50,000 meioses or less, would give a distance under 20 Å, which strongly suggests simultaneous action. This hypothesis is supported by the fact that biotin is not synthesized when two of the mutants are brought together in a culture, in a heterokaryon, or even in a diploid (for it is possible to construct diploid *Aspergillus nidulans*). It is, therefore, not sufficient that the two genes should be in the same nucleus. They must be at a molecular distance in the same chromosome. This condition may not always hold in the Diptera, where homologous chromosomes pair in somatic cells. Recent work on both plants and animals, not all published, shows that a number of genes supposed to be allelomorphic have this type of relation with one another. The three Aspergillus genes are all presumably concerned in making 7-8-diaminopelargonic acid. A further analysis of the process, perhaps indicating the parts played by each, would clearly be of the greatest interest, but it will be very hard to ensure that two mutants are present in one chromosome.

Probably such conditions are quite common, though undetected, in Neurospora. Thus three "allelomorphs" at the locus *pyr-3* are

---

* Pontecorvo assumes a somewhat greater length. I should prefer to assume a shorter one, say 10 μ, for the extended chromosome.

H

known (cf. Table 7). Houlahan and Mitchell (1947) concluded that they were allelomorphs because they did not produce prototrophic heterokaryons and because heterozygotes gave 15, 59 and 100 asci without recombination. On similar evidence Roper's three genes would have been considered allelomorphic. It is of interest that all four "pyrimidineless" loci in Neurospora are in the same chromosome arm, within 38 units. They can hardly be in contact, but such close proximity would make it easier for them to act in series.

If such cases are at all frequent we can understand why some, but not the majority, of genes undergo "position" effects, their functions being altered by chromosomal arrangements. Such relations are, of course, known on a macroscopic scale. The thyroid gland will perform almost if not quite all its normal functions when transplanted to a variety of sites; the pituitary will not do so, but requires a special portal blood supply.

Many genes may act locally, transforming substrates of low molecular weight at millimicromolar rates. To the biochemist they would appear as desmo-enzymes. So far as I know no attempt has been made to bring such "insoluble" enzymes into solution with desoxy-ribo-nuclease. Such an attempt, if successful, might throw a good deal of light on biochemical genetics even though it would almost certainly fail if, as in Roper's case, it would lead to the dissociation of the catalyst.

Another type of work which throws some light on localization is that of Billingham and Medawar (1948) on transplants. When skin is transplanted from a coloured to a white area of the same guinea-pig, the pigment-forming dendritic skin cells of the white area are slowly "infected" by their coloured neighbours, and acquire the capacity to produce pigment. This is at any rate the most probable interpretation of their results. It is highly probable that this "infecting" agent is extranuclear. Piebaldness in guinea-pigs is mainly due to a recessive gene *s*. In a *ss* guinea-pig some dendritic cells possess the complete equipment for pigment formation. Others lack an extranuclear component which is self-propagating and can pass from one cell to another. But (unless piebaldness is due to somatic gene mutation, which is unlikely though not impossible) these are cells of the same genotype. It is to be noted that Billingham and Medawar rather carefully refrain from describing the infecting agent as an enzyme. It may be an enzyme or something a good deal more complicated.

There is, then, a prima facie case that some fairly rare cell constituents, such as the B vitamins, are primary gene products. Let us now consider the case of the larger molecules with which we dealt in Chapter II. Callan and Tomlin (1950) find that the "resting" nucleus of amphibian oocytes is surrounded by two membranes. The outer one, which is soluble in phosphate, has large pores about 400 Å in diameter. The inner one is impermeable to large colloids, the limiting molecular weight being about 2,000. The nuclear sap contains fairly normal proteins, giving no excess of basic amino-acids on chromatograms after hydrolysis. These are, of course, giant nuclei, and may not be typical, but they are in cells which are growing rapidly. If they are typical, it seems unlikely that the nucleus is responsible for the synthesis of the cytoplasmic proteins. There is strong evidence from other sources that they are largely synthesized by extranuclear granules containing ribonucleic acid. It may, however, be the case that the genes synthesize medium-sized molecules whose molecular weight is of the order of 1,000, which are then built up into very large protein and polysaccharide molecules in the cyto-plasm, the proteins probably by ribonucleoproteins (cf. Brachet, 1949). It must, of course, be realized that there is no evidence for a nuclear membrane in bacteria; their nuclei are only just being recognized. We can imagine the genes being responsible for the prosthetic groups of enzymes, the machine tools, so to say, while the main bulk is made by comparatively unspecialized catalysts, but this is not readily reconciled with the facts about haemoglobin discussed in Chapter I. Even if we accept such a hypothesis we need not suppose that certain types of biochemical work are never performed outside the nucleus. Just as Feulgen-positive (DNA) particles are found outside it, activities usually carried on within it may sometimes be carried on in the cytoplasm.

The genes may, I think, legitimately be regarded as intracellular organs (Haldane, 1920). That is to say, the conceptions, and to some extent the technique, of large-scale physiology may be applied to them. We can, of course, also regard them from a more biochemical point of view, as catalysts with many of the properties of ordinary enzymes. Either point of view should lead us to take a broader view of their physiology. We shall, for example, expect their actions to be sometimes at least reversible. The same gene may produce a substance of which there is a shortage, and destroy it if it is in excess. This may be why some of the fungal auxotrophic mutants are so sensitive to substrate concentration. They can neither make an amino-acid if it is absent nor destroy it if too much is present. We shall certainly be prepared for the notion that they may be altered by their function, like other organs; but to assume, as Lysenko and Hinshelwood do, that this alteration will be adaptive on the one hand, and transmissible by the hereditary or copying process for an indefinite period on the other, is unjustifiable. Some organs, such as muscles, grow with use, others, such as teeth, are worn away. Nicotinic acid is certainly used up in the process of catalysis. So apparently are some enzymes, while others are protected by their substrate. But until a learned character is transmitted even by microconidia in a fungus, let alone through spermatozoa in an animal, I shall remain sceptical as to whether heritable adaptive alterations often occur in genes, though they undoubtedly occur elsewhere.

It is, however, clear that this question is most likely to be answered satisfactorily in fungi which on the one hand are sexual, and on the other form small spores with relatively little cytoplasm. The asexual sporulation acts as a sieve which so far has removed all traces of training, whether to use a new substitute, to do without a nutrient, or to resist a poison. It certainly lets through the genes, apparently with a minimum of cytoplasm. If (as is quite likely) a case is found where training is transmitted through such asexual spores, its behaviour during the sexual process should be further studied. Higher plants are less satisfactory material, for few give more than an annual generation, and even plastids, let alone smaller extranuclear constituents, can be carried over by pollen tubes. It is, of course, possible that the data exist in some work published in the Soviet Union which would decide the question, but many of the workers there do not believe in genes, and thus think that there is no question to answer; and in my own case linguistic difficulties prevent me from studying the vast amount of work published on the effects of training in higher plants and their hereditary transmission. Unfortunately the works translated into English never contain the details which are essential for a critical approach. Bacteria are even less suitable material, because large amounts of extranuclear material are transmitted at each cell division, and even where a sexual process exists, its details are far from clear. Even with fungi it will be necessary to make very critical experiments to distinguish between training and selection.

Our survey has shown, I think, why the *a priori* arguments of Lysenko and Hinshelwood for adaptive modification of genes carry less weight than appears at first sight. If, say, a cow is heavily fed and heavily milked, her metabolism is altered. For example, she synthesizes a great deal more fat, and not all this synthesis occurs in her mammary glands. Various enzymes are doing more work than usual. Very few cellular enzymes are working at their full capacity in normal cells, so although some enzymes are probably produced in abnormally large quantities, the increase in their amount is not likely to be proportional to the extra metabolic work; but it is likely that some genes in some nuclei are performing a bit more synthesis than usual. So, presumably, are the normal genes in heterozygotes for a recessive mutant, but there is no evidence that this produces heritable changes in them, and good evidence that it does not when the mutant is incompletely recessive. Further, there is probably very little increase in the synthetic activity of genes in oogonial nuclei of the heavily fed and milked cows. If genes were directly concerned in primary metabolic processes we might expect them to respond as extra-nuclear enzymes do. One reason why they are so little altered is that they are not directly concerned in primary metabolic processes. This is, perhaps, an important adaptive character. The nucleus, which is the part of a cell most shielded from the environment, contains those biochemical "mechanisms" in which adaptive change is least needed in response to environmental changes, and this fact gives the cell a stability in the face of external changes which it might otherwise lack.

Let us try to obtain a little more light on the possible functions of genes. The chromosomes, at any rate, consist largely of nucleoprotein. Now nucleotides, so far always ribonucleotides or ribitol-nucleotides, and not desoxyribonucleotides, and related substances, appear in three contexts, as acceptors and donors of energy-rich phosphate groups, for example adenosine-diphosphoric acid; as donors and acceptors of hydrogen, for example co-enzymes I and II, flavine mononucleotide, and adenine-flavine dinucleotide; and as acceptor and donor of acetyl, e.g. coenzyme A, which is a compound of pantothenic and adenylic acids with other residues. There is no reason at all to think that this list is exhaustive, and we have little idea what common properties these substances possess, which make them efficient catalysts. If we had, we might be able to guess why chromosomes are of the composition that they are. Even the discovery of a single type of catalytically active molecule containing desoxyribose might give us a clue. Another suggestive fact is the probable presence in chromosomes, particularly in their phase as protamine-nucleic acid compounds in fish spermatozoa, of numerous arginine-phosphate bonds. Thus arginine phosphate, like the nucleotides, can be regarded as a fragment of nucleoprotein, and it is possible that these phosphate groups bonding arginine to desoxyribose are energy-rich.

Thus the chromosomes appear to be built of material well adapted for catalytic functions of several different kinds. We have seen reason to suggest that they are particularly concerned in the synthesis of molecules of moderate size. They also synthesize copies of themselves, but there is little evidence which would enable us to bring these two functions together.

On the whole the search for enzymes in nuclei has been disappointing. Apart from phosphatases, they are not very active enzymatically. In particular they show very little oxidative activity. To my mind this is to be expected. If the chromosomes, and the genes on them (if the distinction has any meaning) catalyse a large number of reactions, mostly synthetic, at the millimicromolar level, very probably deriving the needed energy from energy-rich phosphorus compounds, we should not expect to find much enzymatic activity. Thousands of catalysts may be present, but only one or two active centres of any particular kind per nucleus. Let us see what this would mean. A milligram of mammalian chromosomal material consists of something like 10^8 haploid chromosome sets, and might have about this number of active centres of any particular catalyst. If each centre were synthesizing a substance of molecular weight 200 at a rate of 1 molecule per second, this would mean a synthesis of about 10^{-7} milligram per hour, which would not be detectable. To put it in another way, one active centre for each 10^{-5} μg is equivalent to the dilution of an enzyme of molecular weight 60,000 with a hundred million times its weight of enzymatically inert material. Bacterial nuclei, if they could be obtained, would be much more favourable material, since there would be about one active centre per 2×10^{-8} μg dry weight, but even so the catalytic activity would be slight. Phage would be a more hopeful source. I do not, of course, deny the possibility of detecting the catalytic activity of genes in isolated nuclear preparations, but I do not think that any of the observations so far made have been either qualitatively or quantitatively adequate to detect the catalytic activity of genes. The chemical isolation of a gene will be a task demanding the combination of pertinacity, patience, and technical skill which characterized Mme Curie, and is perhaps more frequent (though exceedingly rare) in women than men. Meanwhile, however, it is curious that the search for catalysts has been rather haphazard. Enzymatic activity, if it exists, in chromosomes or viruses is probably mainly synthetic. It would seem reasonable to test phage or other virus for activity in protein synthesis, which would perhaps first be recognized as transpeptidase activity. Similarly it would be of interest to see whether, in any circumstances, whole chromosomes can act as acceptors of energy-rich phosphate from adenosine-triphosphoric acid or other possible donors.

One more point may be made. During mitosis and meiosis the chromosomes move in characteristic manners. Some of these movements are imposed on them passively, as when they are drawn towards the poles at anaphase, apparently by the contraction of "spindle-fibres" attached to their centromeres. Others appear to be autonomous. In particular they coil and uncoil in very characteristic manners (cf. Darlington, 1937). Such movements are to be expected if they contain adenosine-triphosphatase, or more accurately one or more of the numerous catalysts which, like those of muscle fibres, can convert the energy of adenosine triphosphate into other forms.

Such speculations as these will, perhaps, be fruitless, but at least they serve to show at how many points the data of genetics and cytogenetics make contact with biochemistry.

It is, I think, clear that we are approaching what should be a critical epoch in biochemical genetics, the time when we can specify what a given gene, or set of closely linked genes, is doing, as accurately as we can specify what an enzyme such as pepsin is doing, even if we do not know the precise details of what happens in either case. It is also, I think, highly probable where the discovery will first be made. It will not be made by studying a gene-controlled process such as the oxidation of homogentisic acid or the synthesis of arginine from ornithine, which can take place at a rate of thousands of molecules per cell per second. Such processes are not directly controlled by genes. They are controlled by enzymes or other catalysts made by the genes. It is not very likely to come from the study of antigens or enzymes even if these turn out to be primary gene products, just because their structures are very complicated. It is most likely to come from a study of the synthesis of molecules of moderate size which are required in comparatively small numbers. These are the molecules that, in organisms such as man, which have lost the capacity for their synthesis, are called vitamins (though ascorbic acid occurs in such large amounts that it is probably not a primary gene product). Thus a comparison of normal fungi with their "vitaminless" mutants should furnish the critical data. In several cases we know the process catalysed, for example the synthesis of thiamine from thiazole and 2,5-dimethyl-cytosine. An intensive search for pseudo-allelism as found by Roper should disclose some cases of it. If so further research could determine just what each gene is doing. Pontecorvo and Roper's discovery may be as fundamental in biochemical genetics as was Harden and Young's separation of apozymase and cozymase in dynamical biochemistry, where it led to the discovery that two distinct catalysts can act simultaneously on the same molecule of substrate.

A few words may be said on the place of biochemical genetics in the study of evolution, and in medicine. All animals so far investigated lack a number of synthetic capacities besides that of photosynthesis. Thus most vertebrates cannot make the B vitamins, many insects cannot make cholesterol. A few parasites cannot make haem. These capacities have, presumably, been lost by mutation, as Neurospora, Aspergillus or Escherichia lose them in the laboratory. From the biochemical point of view such losses can be regarded as degenerative. However, once such a capacity is lost, the descendants of the organism which has lost it must obtain the substances in question by saprophytism, by eating other organisms, or by keeping them in their gut or some other organ as symbionts. Either of these latter modes of life implies morphological specialization and probably, as we shall see, biochemical specialization. Saprophytism has been exploited by some fungi and protozoa, but implies no evolutionary advance above the bacterial level. Being a herbivore or a carnivore emphatically does. Many species of fungi and green plants have evolved their own peculiar synthesis of substances of medium molecular weight. I think especially of the remarkable range of products of various moulds, of which Raistrick (1950) has given so admirable a summary. Some fungi are almost human in their synthetic preferences, introducing chlorine atoms into organic molecules. As Raistrick points out, they offer an extremely fruitful field for genetical study. The higher plants have also pioneered in the synthesis of anthocyanins, anthoxanthins, glycosides, and alkaloids. Here we have at least the beginnings of an evolutionary genetics. We can say, for example, that a plant which produces a delphinidin derivative rather than a cyanidin derivative is probably in that respect at least less primitive.

The animals have made less progress with the synthesis of crystalloids, though they have displayed a remarkable ability in producing inorganic substances, among their *tours de force* being the silica skeletons of sponges and the calcite crystals of echinoderm tests; but there is good reason to think that they may be far ahead of the higher plants, let alone bacteria and fungi, in the synthesis of specific colloids, and particularly proteins. A higher animal has a great many more different sorts of cells than a higher plant, and this specificity, which is a prerequisite for morphological complexity, appears to have a biochemical basis. The differences must be mainly in large molecules, particularly proteins and polysaccharides. A human haploid nucleus contains 300 times as much nucleic acid as a bacterial nucleus, and perhaps about 300 times as many genes. I suggest that most of these genes are concerned in the synthesis of large molecules such as enzymes, even if they do not carry out such syntheses completely, the later stages being controlled by extranuclear ribonucleoproteins. If this view is correct, the view that animals can be regarded as in any way "degenerate" is due to the fact that biochemists have inevitably got further with the study of crystalloids than with that of colloids.

So far from the higher organisms showing any tendency to biochemical simplification, they show a strong, and at present unexplained, drive towards biochemical complexity. It is well known that inbreeding is harmful to most animal and plant species, and many have the most elaborate devices, from the heterostyly of the primrose to the "Table of Kindred and Affinity" of the Prayer Book to avoid it. The result of inbreeding is to produce homozygosis, that of outbreeding to produce heterozygosis, and there is good evidence, both direct and indirect, which cannot be given here, that heterozygotes for genes at a great many loci are fitter than homozygotes. This means that among the higher plants and animals there is natural selection in favour of biochemical complexity. This is so although, among mammals at least, antigenic diversity, which leads to incompatibility between mother and foetus, is decidedly harmful (cf. Medawar, 1953). Possible reasons for this can be imagined. A biochemically homogeneous enzyme may have a sharp optimum for pH, salt requirements, and so on. A pair of such enzymes will have a wider zone, and so on. In fact a number of enzymes have been found by Gillespie, Jermyn, and Woods (1952) to consist of several constituents separable in an electric field. Such a mixed enzyme would be a definite advantage in an organism either subjected to a wide range of environments or with a variety of chemically differentiated tissues. This explanation is, of course, speculative. The drive towards biochemical diversity is a fact. Indeed the evidence for greater fitness of heterozygotes is stronger than that for most other kinds of natural selection. However, heterozygosis can usually only secure complexity at about half the gene loci where it is desirable in any one individual. To secure it in all individuals either the whole set of chromosomes must be doubled, or small sections of chromosomes must be doubled. Both these events occur in evolution. It is not without interest that in Paramecium, the only protozoan whose genetics have been seriously studied, most individuals are homozygotes, so the drive towards biochemical complexity found in Metazoa and Metaphyta is absent. Perhaps that is why they have not evolved further.

I suggest then that the drive towards biochemical complexity is a major evolutionary trend, that many other trends are probably by-products of it, one of these being the apparently useless development of morphological complexity in many organisms. Such men as Darwin, who proved the advantages of outbreeding experimentally, and J. S. Haldane and J. Barcroft, who studied individual variations in a protein, were alike laying the foundations of evolutionary biochemistry. If this is correct, while the study of crystalloids may long remain important in the genetics of bacteria and fungi, that of colloids will be absolutely necessary for the understanding of the genetics of higher animals, and in particular of the genetics of their morphogenesis.

It is possible that when a history, however sketchy, of biochemical evolution can be drawn up, it will fall into four parts. If Haldane's (1928) suggestion, later developed by Oparin and others, that the most primitive organisms obtained their free energy from metastable organic molecules synthesized by solar ultraviolet radiation in the absence of molecular oxygen, be accepted, the earliest organisms were definitely auxotrophic. They required a variety of preformed organic molecules, probably including sugars. The first few syntheses which they could perform would be those of complex catalysts, and as Horowitz (1945) suggested, they would develop chains of syntheses in the opposite order to that in which the synthesis occurs. It is not so clear that this principle holds after the first stage.

Photosynthesis would be of little advantage to an organism which could not build all or almost all the required molecules from phosphoglyceric acid, or whatever may be the primary product of photosynthesis. The second stage of evolution would, perhaps, have been rather rapid and catastrophic, namely the perfection of photosynthesis, and the adaptation of some types to life in an atmosphere containing oxygen, while others died out.

Simultaneously or subsequently to this, a third stage involved the utilization of energy derived from oxidations by molecular oxygen. There may, of course, have been anaerobic animals which obtained the energy needed for obtaining food by merely fermenting it, but clearly the capacity for oxidizing it fairly fully and utilizing the energy so obtained would confer an immense advantage. We are still extremely ignorant of the comparative biochemistry of oxidation. The citric acid cycle, though it furnishes most of the energy in vertebrates, may not do so in all invertebrates, let alone in plant roots.

The multicellular plants have probably always needed molecular oxygen at some stage in their life cycles, if only the flagellate stage, and there may be no more perfect mechanisms for its use in the root of an oak tree than in the zoospore of an alga, but the oxidative mechanisms have probably evolved to some extent in the last few hundred million years.

The fourth stage has been a stage of adaptive radiation, accompanied by some loss of function in all organisms but the photosynthesizing plants, but also by considerable increases in synthetic capacities in all or almost all groups. It will be of the greatest interest to investigate certain mutations to see whether they really give rise to new adventures in metabolism. Most such adventures would, of course, be useless or worse, like such morphogenetic adventures as polydactyly and the formation of giant Pacinian corpuscles in neurofibromatosis, both due to dominant genes. Chronic porphyria and xyloketosuria in man may be such adventures. Catcheside (1949) discusses "suppressor" mutations in Drosophila which restore functions lost by other mutations. Thus a suppressor of *vermilion* restores the capacity to make kynurenine from tryptophan, but also suppresses extra melanin formation due to other mutants. "These non-specific suppressors can hardly act in any way other than to alter the cellular environment so that the mutant enzymes are inactivated" (Catcheside, 1949). There are, perhaps, other possibilities, such as the formation of a not very specific oxidase, which would attack both tryptophan and a melanin precursor.

I suggest that progressive biochemical evolution has not been by making enzymes or genes of a radically new character, but by broadening and narrowing their ranges of specificity, so that one enzyme in an ancestral form would be represented by a battery of enzymes in a descendant, which could be regarded as descendants of the original enzyme.

If I am right in believing that there is at least a correlation between morphological and biochemical diversity, the study of biochemical evolution, based as it must be almost wholly on living organisms, may not be as hopeless a task as has been sometimes assumed.

In dealing with the relations of biochemical genetics to medicine I would first refer readers to Dr. Harris' monograph. Secondly, I would refer them to any work of forty years ago on biochemistry, or physiological chemistry, as it was then called. Much of it would be an account of the chemistry of foods and urine, and of the overall

exchanges of the body, for example its carbon and nitrogen balances. Most of the data on intermediary metabolism were drawn from the study of diabetes, a metabolic error which was not only common in man, but could be produced in animals by pancreatectomy or effectively by phlorizin. This study had disclosed both the existence of intermediary metabolites such as aceto-acetic acid which escaped oxidation in diabetes, and the highly specific nature of the metabolism of the amino-acids, some of which were glycogenic, other ketogenic, in a diabetic mammal. Except for a few data on detoxication, remarkably little else was known about intermediary metabolism, or as it is now often called, dynamic biochemistry. If readers turn to Garrod's (1909) "Inborn errors of metabolism" they will find a much more modern point of view. I quote some passages. "As far as our present knowledge of them enables us to judge they apparently result from failure of some step or other in the series of chemical changes which we call metabolism, and are in this respect most nearly analogous to what are known as malformations by defect."
"The view is daily gaining ground that each successive step in the building up and breaking down, not merely of proteins, carbo-hydrates, and fats in general, but even of individual fractions of proteins and of individual sugars, is the work of special enzymes set apart for each particular purpose. . . . If any one step in the process fail the intermediate product in being at the point of arrest will escape further change, just as when the film of a biograph is brought to a standstill the moving figures are left foot in air. All that is known of the course of catabolism tends to show that in such circumstances the intermediate product in being is wont to be excreted as such, rather than that it is further dealt with along abnormal lines." "It was pointed out by Bateson, and has recently been emphasized by Punnett, that the mode of incidence of alkapto-nuria finds a ready explanation if the anomaly in question be regarded as a rare recessive character in the Mendelian sense." "Upon chemical as upon structural variations, the factors which make for evolution have worked and are working."

Garrod described human albinism, alkaptonuria, cystinuria, and pentosuria, both from a biochemical and a genetical point of view, and hoped that similar studies would throw a great deal of light "upon the chemical processes at work in the normal human organism." In fact this light came largely from the study of enzymes, made possible above all by Sörensen's work on pH. A large number of enzymes are comparatively easy to study, and we have an outline of some parts of dynami biochemistry; but there are conspicuous gaps, notably our almost complete ignorance as to protein synthesis.

The study of inborn errors of metabolism has in fact given us a mass of information on biochemical processes, in particular the synthesis of the amino-acids in Neurospora, the brilliant work of the American school described in Chapter III. It has not given us a great deal about human biochemistry. This is partly because the abnormal types are not readily come by, partly because the biochemists who studied them have been disciples of Hopkins rather than of J. S. Haldane, whose outlook is peculiarly adapted for studying minor variations of function round a normal level. The work of Neuberger on porphyria referred to in Chapter VI is perhaps nearer to the tradition of J. S. Haldane than is that of most other workers in this field. I, personally, believe that the future of biochemical genetics applied to medicine is largely in the study of diatheses and idiosyncrasies, differences of innate make-up which do not necessarily lead to disease, but may do so. I may well be wrong. It is, for example, possible that tissue transplantation may become as practicable as blood transfusion. If so we shall have to specify as precisely as possible the differences between Mr. A's and Mr. B's organs. It is also possible that the inevitably increased interest in geriatrics will confirm the suggestion which I have made elsewhere (Haldane, 1941) that "natural" death is largely due to lethal genes acting so late in life as to be almost immune to natural selection. If so we shall become interested in innate biochemical differences which lead to the development of arteriosclerosis, various forms of cancer, and other diseases of old age.

To sum up, then, we have learned that genes control biochemical processes. The control observed is generally remote; for example, through an enzyme synthesized wholly or in part by the genes in question. We are still never sure that we can isolate primary gene products, though it is likely that this has been done. Our present picture of dynamical biochemistry, as given in such a work as that of Baldwin (1952), is largely confined to the processes in which relatively large amounts of energy are transferred, for example the exchange of hydrogen atom pairs or active phosphate groups, or those which lead up to them, such as the isomerization of citric acid. The only synthesis of a colloidal molecule even roughly understood is that of starch or glycogen. We know very little about the detailed transformation of the rarer molecular species. The genetical picture suggests that a good deal of the synthesis, and perhaps other kinds of transformation of the rarer molecular types, takes place in the nucleus, which may be regarded as something like a machine-tool shop where highly specialized individual craftsmen are at work. It may turn out that these processes follow the same general pattern as the cytoplasmic processes so far studied. It may be, for example, that adenosine-triphosphoric acid will be found to play as great a part within the nucleus as outside. It may be, to suggest just one possibility, that within the nucleus desoxyribose-adenosine-phosphoric acid residues are anchored, and act locally.

In the last twenty years we have learned something of the metabolic origin and fate of molecules which have mostly been known for fifty or a hundred years, such as glucose, glycerol, pyruvate, acetoacetate, tyrosine, cystine, and so on. We naturally know much less about the origin and fate of those which have only been discovered in the last fifty years, such as the vitamins and the enzymes. I believe that their origin, at least, is largely within the nucleus. In the study of this origin I believe that the conception of the gene will be a fruitful guide. The gene was originally conceived as something which behaved as a unit in meiosis. Bateson and Punnett used the word "factor" which has much to commend it.

As the study of mutation developed geneticists tended to think of the gene as something which mutated as a unit, even when two neighbouring genes, like *scute* and *yellow* in *Drosophila melanogaster*, hardly ever separated in normal meiosis. As we learn more of the functions of genes we shall probably come to regard them rather as the "active centres" of Quastel, located at definite points on a chromosome. It may be that in time they will fade out as, according to some physical theories, electrons are fading into probability distributions. It may also be that their individuality will be reasserted. Thirty years ago some biochemists were saying that the attempt to follow an individual proton was not only practically but theoretically impossible. Since then we have used deuterons, and followed them up. As a disciple of Hopkins I believe that biochemists should attempt to trace the fate of individual molecules and atoms. If they do so they will be brought to recognize that the chemical structure of the chromosomes is as detailed as that of a book or a picture, and that the key to a knowledge of that structure is the science of genetics.

BIBLIOGRAPHY

ADELBERG, E. A., BONNER, D. M., and TATUM, E. L.
  1951. *J. Biol. Chem.*, **190**, 839.
ANNISON, F. F., and MORGAN, W. T. J.
  1952. *Biochem. J.*, **50**, 460.
AUERBACH, C.
  1949. *Biol. Rev.*, **24**, 355.
AUERBACH, C., and ROBSON, J. M.
  1942. Report to Ministry of Supply.
  1947. *Proc. Roy. Soc. Edin.*, **62**, 271, 284.
AVERY, O. T., MACLEOD, C. M., and MACCARTY, M.
  1944. *J. Exp. Med.*, **79**, 137.
BALDWIN, E.
  1952. *Dynamic Aspects of Biochemistry.* Cambridge.
BARCROFT, J.
  1928. *The Respiratory Function of the Blood*, Vol. 2. Cambridge.
BEADLE, G. W.
  1945. *Chem. Rev.*, **37**, 15.
BEALE, G. H.
  1941. *J. Genet.*, **42**, 197.
  1952. *Genetics*, **37**, 62.
BECKER, E.
  1942. *Zeit. ind. Abst.-u-Vererb.-*, **80**, 157.
BILLINGHAM, R. E., and MEDAWAR, P. B.
  1948. *Heredity*, **2**, 49.
BIRD, M. J.
  1952. *J. Genet.*, **50**, 480.
BITTNER, J. J.
  1939. *Am. J. Clin. Path.*, **7**, 430.
BOIVIN, A., VENDRELY, R., and LE HOULT, Y.
  1945. *C.R. Acad. Sci.*, **221**, 646.
BOIVIN, A., VENDRELY, R., and TULASNE, R.
  1949. *Unités biologiques douées de continuité génétique*, 67.
BONNER, D. M.
  1946a. *Am. J. Bot.*, **33**, 788.
  1946b. *J. Biol. Chem.*, **166**, 4545.
  1948. *Proc. Nat. Ac. Sci.*, **34**, 5.
BONNER, D. M., and YANOFSKY, C.
  1949. *Proc. Nat. Ac. Sci.*, **35**, 5761.
BONNER, D. M., YANOFSKY, C., and PARTRIDGE, C. W. H.
  1952. *Proc. Nat. Ac. Sci.*, **38**, 25.
BOREK, E., and WAELSCH, H.
  1951. *J. Biol. Chem.*, **190**, 191.

BRACHET, J.
1949. *Unités biologiques douées de continuité génétique.*
BRANSON, H., and BANKS, L. D.
1952. *Science,* **115,** 84.
BRIDEL, M., and BOURDOUIL, C.
1932. *Bull. Soc. Chim. biol.,* **14,** 214.
BUTENANDT, A., and ALBRECHT, W.
1952. *Zeit. Naturforsch.,* **7b,** 287.
BUTENANDT, A., WEIDEL, W., WEICHERT, R., and DERJUGIN, W.
1943. *Zeit. physiol. Chem.,* **279,** 29.
CALLAN, F. G., and TOMLIN, J. G.
1950. *Proc. Roy. Soc., B.,* **137,** 367.
CAMERON, J. W., and TEAS, H. J.
1948. *Proc. Nat. Ac. Sci.,* **34,** 390.
CARR, J. G.
1950. *Biochem. Soc. Symp.,* **4,** 25.
CASPARI, E.
1949. *Quart. Rev. Biol.,* **24,** 185.
CATCHESIDE, D. G.
1949. *The Genetics of Micro-organisms.* London.
CHASE, H. B.
1950. *Genetics,* **35,** 101.
CHASE, H. B., GUNTHER, M. S., MILLER, J., and WOLFSON, D.
1947. *Science,* **107,** 297.
COHN, M., and TORRIANI, A. M.
1951. *C.R. Ac. Sci.,* **232,** 115.
CONGER, A. D., and FAIRCHILD, L. M.
1952. *Proc. Nat. Ac. Sci.,* **38,** 284.
COUTAGNE, G.
1903. *Bull. Sci. France et Belg.,* **37,** 1.
VAN CREVELD, S.
1952. *Arch. Dis. Children,* **27,** 113.
CUÉNOT, L.
1903. *Comptes Rendus Soc. de Biol.,* **55,** 301.
DARLINGTON, C. D.
1937. *Recent Advances in Cytology.* London.
1949. *Unités biologiques douées de continuité génétique,* 123.
DAVIS, B. D.
1948. *J. Am. Chem. Soc.,* **70,** 4267.
1952. *Nature,* **169,** 534.
DEAN, A. C. R., and HINSHELWOOD, SIR C.
1952. *Proc. Roy. Soc., B.,* **139,** 236.
DEANESLEY, R., and PARKES, A. S.
1937. *Quart. J. Exp. Physiol.,* **26,** 393.
DELBRUCK, M.
1949. *Unités biologiques douées de continuité génétique,* 91.

DEMEREC, M.
  1953. *Symp. Soc. Exp. Biol.*, **6**, 43.
DOUGLAS, C. D., HALDANE, J. S., and HALDANE, J. B. S.
  1912. *Journ. Physiol.*, **44**, 275.
EDSALL, J. T.
  1947. *Advances in Protein Chemistry*, **3**, 466.
EMERSON, S.
  1944. *Proc. Nat. Ac. Sci.*, **30**, 179.
  1947. *J. Bact.*, **54**, 195.
  1950. *Cold Spring Harbor Sympos. Quant. Biol.*, **14**, 40.
ENKLEWITZ, M., and LASKER, M.
  1935. *J. Biol. Chem.*, **110**, 443.
EPHRUSSI, B.
  1949. *Unités biologiques douées de continuité génétique*, 165.
EPHRUSSI, B., and SLONIMSKY.
  1950. *Biochem. et Biophys. Acta*, **7**, 563.
FABERGÉ, A. C., and BEALE, G. H.
  1942. *J. Genet.*, **43**, 121.
FILITTI-WURMSER, S., and JACQUOT-ARMAND, Y.
  1947. *Arch. Sci. Physiol.*, **1**, 151.
FILITTI-WURMSER, S., JACQUOT-ARMAND, Y., and WURMSER, R.
  1950. *Journ. Chim. Phys.*, **47**, 419.
  1951. *C.R. Ac. Sci.*, **232**, 2484.
  1952. *Journ. Chim. Phys.*, **49**, 550.
FINCHAM, J. R. S.
  1950. *J. Biol. Chem.*, **182**, 61.
FOSTER, M.
  1951. *J. Exp. Zool.*, **117**, 211.
FOX, A. L.
  1932. *Proc. Nat. Ac. Sci.*, **18**, 115.
FOX, H. M.
  1945. *Nature*, **156**, 18.
FRIEDENREICH, V., and HARTMANN, C.
  1948. *Zts. f. Immunitätsforsch.*, **92**, 141.
FRIEDMAN, M., and BYERS, S. O.
  1948. *J. Biol. Chem.*, **175**, 2727.
FRIEDRICH-FREKSA, H.
  1940. *Naturwiss.*, **28**, 376.
FRIES, N.
  1947. *Nature*, **159**, 199.
FRIES, N., and KIHLMANN, B.
  1948. *Nature*, **162**, 573.
GARROD, A. E.
  1909. *Inborn Errors of Metabolism*. Oxford.
GIBSON, Q. H.
  1948. *Biochem. J.*, **42**, 13.

I

GILLESPIE, J. M., JERMYN, M. A., and WOODS, F. F.
  1952. *Nature*, **169**, 487.
GOLDSCHMIDT, R.
  1916. *Science*, **43**, 98.
  1938. *Physiological Genetics*. New York.
GORER, P. A.
  1938. *J. Path. Bact.*, **47**, 231.
  1947. *Canc. Res.*, **7**, 634.
GRAM, H. C.
  1932. *Act. Med. Scand.*, **78**, 268.
GRAY, C. H., MUIR, I. M. H., and NEUBERGER, A.
  1950. *Biochem. J.*, **47**, 452.
GRAY, C. H., and NEUBERGER, A.
  1950. *Biochem. J.*, **47**, 81.
GRAY, C. H., NEUBERGER, A., and SNEATH, P. H. A.
  1950. *Biochem. J.*, **47**, 87.
GREEN, M. M.
  1947. *Genetics*, **34**, 564.
GRUBB, R.
  1948. *Nature*, **162**, 933.
GRÜNEBERG, H.
  1947. *Animal Genetics and Medicine*. London.
  1952. *The Genetics of the Mouse*. The Hague.
HADDOW, A.
  1949. *Proc. 1st Nat. Cancer Conference*, 88.
HALDANE, J. B. S.
  1920. *Trans. Oxford Univ. Junior Scientific Club*. 3rd Series, **1**, 3.
  1928. *Rationalist Annual*. Reprinted in *The Inequality of Man*, London.
  1930. *Enzymes*. London.
  1933. *Nature*, **132**, 265.
  1941. *New Paths in Genetics*. London.
  1948. *Proc. Roy. Soc., B.*, **135**, 147.
HALDANE, J. S., and PRIESTLEY, J. G.
  1935. *Respiration*. Oxford.
HARRIS, H.
  1949. *Ann. Eugen.*, **14**, 293.
  1950. *Ann. Eugen.*, **15**, 95.
  1953. *An Introduction to Human Biochemical Genetics*. Galton Laboratory Monographs. London (in press).
HARRIS, J. W.
  1950. *Proc. Soc. exp. Biol. Med.*, **75**, 197.
HASKINS, F. A., and MITCHELL, H. K.
  1949. *Proc. Nat. Ac. Sci.*, **35**, 500
HAYES, W.
  1952a. *Nature*, **169**, 118.
  1952b. *Nature*, **169**, 1017.

HINSHELWOOD, C. N.
  1950. *Proc. Roy. Soc.*, **137**, 88.
HINTON, T., ELLIS, J., and NOYES, D. T.
  1951. *Proc. Nat. Ac. Sci.*, **37**, 293.
HÖRLEIN, H., and WEBER, G.
  1948. *Deutsch. med. Wochschr.*, **73**, 876.
HOROWITZ, N. H.
  1945. *Proc. Nat. Ac. Sci.*, **31**, 153.
  1947. *Biol. Chem.*, **171**, 255.
  1950. *Advances in Genetics*, **3**, 33.
HOTCHKISS, R. D.
  1949. *Unités biologiques douées de continuité génétique*, 57.
HOULAHAN, M. B., and MITCHELL, H. K.
  1947. *Proc. Nat. Ac. Sci.*, **33**, 223.
  1948a. *Arch. Biochem.*, **19**, 257.
  1948b. *Proc. Nat. Ac. Sci.*, **34**, 465.
IRWIN, M. R.
  1947. *Advances in Genetics*, **1**, 133.
ITANO, H. A.
  1951. *Proc. Nat. Ac. Sci.*, **37**, 775.
ITANO, H. A., and NEEL, J. V.
  1950. *Proc. Nat. Ac. Sci.*, **36**, 613.
JERMOLJEVA, Z., and BUJANOWSKA, L.
  1927. *Zentr. f. Bakt.*, **24**, 477.
JUCCI, C.
  1944. *Introduzione allo studio della Genetica per Medici, Agrari, e
      Naturalisti*. Milano.
  1949. *Proc. 8th Int. Cong. Genetics*, 286.
KALMUS, H.
  1941. *Proc. Roy. Soc., B.*, **130**, 185.
KHANOLKAR, W. R., and CHITRE, R. G.
  1944. *Canc. Res.*, **4**, 128.
KILKENNY, B. C., and HINSHELWOOD, SIR C.
  1951. *Proc. Roy. Soc., B.*, **139**, 73.
  1952. *Proc. Roy. Soc., B.*, **139**, 578.
KING, E. D., SCHNEIDERMAN, H. A., and SAX, K. A.
  1952. *Proc. Nat. Ac. Sci.*, **38**, 34.
KNOX, W. F., and MEHLER, A. H.
  1950. *J. Biol. Chem.*, **187**, 429.
KÜHN, R.
  1923. *Zeit. physiol. Chem.*, **127**, 234.
LAWRENCE, W. J. C.
  1950. *Biochem. Sioc. Symp.*, **4**, 3.
LAWRENCE, W. J. C., and PRICE, J. R.
  1940. *Biol. Rev.*, **15**, 35.

LEDERBERG, J.
1948. *Genetics*, **33**, 617.
1949. *Proc. Nat. Ac. Sci.*, **35**, 178.
LEIN, J., and LEIN, P. S.
1952. *Proc. Nat. Ac. Sci.*, **38**, 44.
LEUCHTENBERGER, C., VENDRELY, R., and VENDRELY, C.
1951. *Proc. Nat. Ac. Sci.*, **37**, 33.
LEWIS, D.
1951. *Proc. Roy. Soc., B.*, **140**, 127.
LEWIS, E. B.
1948. *Genetics*, **33**, 113.
LINDEGREN, C. C.
1945. *Ann. Miss. Bot. Gard.*, **32**, 107.
1949. *The Yeast Cell, Its Genetics and Cytology*. St. Louis.
LITTLE, C. C.
1914. *Science*, **40**, 904.
LORING, H. S., and PIERCE, J. G.
1944. *J. Biol. Chem.*, **153**, 61.
LWOFF, A.
1944. *L'évolution physiologique*. Paris.
1949. *Unités biologiques douées de continuité génétique*, 7.
LYSENKO, T. D.
1949. *The Situation in Biological Science*. Moscow.
MCILWAIN, H.
1946. *Nature*, **158**, 198.
1949. *Proc. Roy. Soc., B.*, **136**, 12.
MACKINNEY, G., and JENKINS, J. A.
1952. *Proc. Nat. Ac. Sci.*, **38**, 48.
MANGELSDORF, P., and FRAPS, G.
1931. *Science*, **73**, 241.
MASON, H. H., and TURNER, M. E.
1938. *Am. Journ. Dis. Child.*, **56**, 359.
MEDAWAR, P. B.
1953. *Symp. Soc. Exp. Biol.* (in press).
MEFFERD, R. B., and MATNEY, T. S.
1952. *Science*, **115**, 116.
METZNER, H.
1952. *Biol. Zent.*, **71**, 257.
MITCHELL, H. K., and HOULAHAN, M. B.
1946. *Fed. Proc.*, **5**, 370.
1947. *Fed. Proc.*, **6**, 506.
1948. *J. Biol. Chem.*, **174**, 883.
MITCHELL, H. K., HOULAHAN, M. B., and NYC, J. F.
1948. *J. Biol. Chem.*, **172**, 525.
MITCHELL, M. B., and MITCHELL, H. K.
1952. *Proc. Nat. Ac. Sci.*, **38**, 442.

MITCHELL, H. K., and NYC, J. F.
  1948. *Proc. Nat. Ac. Sci.*, **34**, 1.
MITCHELSON, A. M., DRELL, W., and MITCHELL, H. K.
  1951. *Proc. Nat. Ac. Sci.*, **37**, 396.
MONOD, J.
  1949. *Unités biologiques douées de continuité génétique*, 181.
  1950. *Biochem. Soc. Symp.*, **4**, 51.
MONOD, J., COHEN-BAZIRE, G., and COHN, M.
  1951. *Biochem. et Biophys. Act.*, **7**, 585.
MONOD, J., and COHN, M.
  1952. *Advances in Enzymology*, **13**, 67.
MORGAN, W. T. J.
  1950. *Nature*, **166**, 300.
MULLER, H. J.
  1932. *Proc. 6th Int. Cong. Genet.*, 213.
  1947. *Proc. Roy. Soc.*, *B.*, **134**, 1.
NEUBERGER, A., RIMINGTON, C., and WILSON, J. M. C.
  1947. *Biochem. J.*, **41**, 438.
NICHOLAS, R. F. H., and RIMINGTON, C.
  1951. *Biochem. J.*, **48**, 306.
OSTERGREN, G., and LEVAN, A.
  1943. *Hereditas*, **29**, 381.
OTTKE, R. C., TATUM, E. L., ZUBIN, I., and BLOCH, C.
  1951. *J. Biol. Chem.*, **189**, 429.
PAULING, L., ITANO, H. A., SINGER, S. J., and WELLS, I. C.
  1949. *Science*, **110**, 543.
PEACOCKE, A. R., and HINSHELWOOD, SIR C.
  1948. *Proc. Roy. Soc.*, *B.*, **135**, 454.
PERUTZ, M. F., LIQUORI, A. M., and ERICH, F.
  1951. *Nature*, **167**, 929.
PERUTZ, M. F., and MITCHISON, J. M.
  1950. *Nature*, **166**, 677.
PLOUGH, H. H., MILLER, H. Y., and BERRY, M. E.
  1951. *Proc. Nat. Ac. Sci.*, **37**, 604.
PONTECORVO, G.
  1952. With sections by J. A. Roper, L. M. Hemmons, K. D. Mac-
        donald, A. W. J. Bufton. *Advances in Genetics*, **5**, 141.
  1952. *Advances in Enzymology*, **13**, 131.
PUNNETT, R. C., and BAILEY, P. G.
  1921. *J. Gen.*, **11**, 37.
RAISTRICK, H.
  1950. *Proc. Roy. Soc.*, *B.*, **136**, 481.
RAPPOPORT, I. A.
  1946. *C.R. Ac. Sci. U.R.S.S.*, **54**, 65.
RAVDIN, R. G., and CRANDALL, D. I.
  1951. *J. Biol. Chem.*, **189**, 137.

RHOADES, M. M.
1949. *Unités biologiques douées de continuité génétique*, 37.
RICH, A.
1952. *Proc. Nat. Ac. Sci.*, **38**, 187.
RIEMAN, G. H.
1931. *J. Agric. Res.*, **42**, 5.
RIMINGTON, C.
1936. *Onderstepoort Jour. Vet. Sci.*, **7**, 567.
RIMINGTON, C., and MILES, P. A.
1951. *Biochem. J.*, **50**, 202.
ROPER, J. A.
1950. *Nature*, **166**, 956.
ROTHMAN, S., KRYSA, H. F., and SMILJANIC, A. M.
1946. *Proc. Soc. exp. Biol. Med.*, **62**, 208.
RUDKIN, G. I., and SCHULTZ, J.
1949. *Proc. 8th Int. Cong. Genetics*, 652.
RUSSELL, L. B., and RUSSELL, W. L.
1948. *Genetics*, **33**, 237.
RUTMAN, R. J.
1951. *Genetics*, **36**, 54.
RUTMAN, R. J., DEMPSTER, E., and TARVER, H.
1949. *J. Biol. Chem.*, **177**, 491.
RYAN, F. J.
1947. *Cold Spring Harbor Symp. Quant. Biol.*, **11**, 215.
RYAN, F. J., and LEDERBERG, J.
1946. *Proc. Nat. Ac. Sci.*, **36**, 163.
SAWIN, P. B., and GLICK, D.
1943. *Proc. Nat. Ac. Sci.*, **29**, 55.
SCHMUCK, A.
1938. *C.R. Ac. Sci. U.R.S.S.*, **22**, 241.
SCHØNE, R.
1944. *Act. path. microb. Scand.*, **21**, 401.
SCHRÖDINGER, E.
1944. *What is Life?* Cambridge.
SCHROEDER, W. A., KAY, L. M., and WELLS, I. C.
1950. *J. Biol. Chem.*, **187**, 221.
SCOTT-MONCRIEFF, R.
1939. *Ergeb. Enzymforsch.*, **8**, 277.
SHAUMYAN, V. A.
1949. *The Situation in Biological Science*, 250. Moscow.
SHENG, T. C., and RYAN, F. J.
1948. *Genetics*, **33**, 221.
SONNEBORN, T. M.
1947. *Advances in Genetics*, **1**, 263.
SPIEGELMAN, S.
1946. *Cold Spring Harbor Symp. Quant. Biol.*, **11**, 256.

SPIEGELMAN, S., and DE LORENZO, W. F.
  1952. *Proc. Nat. Ac. Sci.*, **38**, 583.
SPIEGELMAN, S., DE LORENZO, W. F., and CAMPBELL, A. M.
  1951. *Proc. Nat. Ac. Sci.*, **37**, 513.
SPIEGELMAN, S., SUSSMAN, R. R., and PINSKER, E.
  1950. *Proc. Nat. Ac. Sci.*, **36**, 591.
SRB, A., and HOROWITZ, N. H.
  1944. *J. Biol. Chem.*, **154**, 129.
STANIER, R. Y.
  1947. *J. Bact.*, **54**, 339.
STONE, W. S., WYSS, O., and HAAS, F.
  1947. *Proc. Nat. Ac. Sci.*, **33**, 59.
SUBRAMANIAM, M. K.
  1945. *Curr. Sci.*, **14**, 234.
TANRET, M. C.
  1935. *Bull. Soc. Chim. biol.*, **17**, 1235.
TATUM, E. L., and ADELBERG, E. A.
  1951. *J. Biol. Chem.*, **190**, 843.
TAYLOR, H. E.
  1949. *Unités biologiques douées de continuité génétique*, 45.
TEAS, H. J.
  1951. *J. Biol. Chem.*, **190**, 369.
TEAS, H. J., and ANDERSON, W. G.
  1951. *Proc. Nat. Ac. Sci.*, **37**, 645.
TEAS, H. J., HOROWITZ, N. H., and FLING, M.
  1948. *J. Biol. Chem.*, **172**, 151.
THODAY, J. M., and READ, J.
  1948. *Nature*, **160**, 608.
TODD, C.
  1930. *Proc. Roy. Soc., B.*, **107**, 197.
TOMLIN, S. G., and CALLAN, H. G.
  1951. *Quart. Journ. microsc. Sci.*, **72**, 221.
TUKE, D., DREW, R., and POLLARD, E.
  1952. *Proc. Nat. Ac. Sci.*, **38**, 180.
UMBARGER, H. E., and ADLEBERG, E. A.
  1951. *J. Biol. Chem.*, **192**, 883.
VENDRELY, R.
  1950. *Bull. Soc. Chem. Biol.*, **32**, 427.
WAGNER, R. R.
  1949. *Proc. Nat. Ac. Sci.*, **35**, 185.
VAN WAGTENDONK, W. J.
  1948. *J. Biol. Chem.*, **173**, 691.
WEIGLE, J. J., and DELBRUCK, M.
  1951. *J. Bact.*, **62**, 301.

WEIR, J. A.
   1949. *J. infect. Dis.*, **84**, 352.
   1950. *Genetics*, **35**, 138.
WENT, F. W., ROSEN, A. L., and ZECHMEISTER, L.
   1942. *Plant Physiol.*, **17**, 41.
WILDMAN, S. G., ABEGG, F. A., ELDER, J. A., and HENDRIKS, S. B.
   1946. *Arch. Biochem.*, **10**, 141.
WILLSTÄTTER, R., KÜHN, R., and SOBOTKA, H.
   1923. *Zeit. physiol. Chem.*, **129**, 33.
WINDSOR, E.
   1951. *J. Biol. Chem.*, **192**, 607.
WINGE, O., and ROBERTS, C.
   1948. *C.R. Lab. Carlsberg. Ser. Physiol.*, **24**, 263.
   1952. *C.R. Lab. Carlsberg*, **25**, 141.
DE WINTON, D., and HALDANE, J. B. S.
   1933. *J. Genet.*, **27**, 1.
WOLLMAN, E., and WOLLMAN, E.
   1925. *C.R. Soc. de Biol.*, **93**, 1568.
WRIGHT, B.
   1951. *Ann. Biochem.*, **31**, 332.
WRIGHT, S.
   1916. *Carn. Inst. Wash. Pub.*, 241.
   1949. *Genetics*, **34**, 245.
WURMSER, R., FILITTI-WURMSER, S., and AUBEL-LESURE, G.
   1952. *C.R. Ac. Sci.*, **234**, 2392.
YUDIN, V. M.
   1949. *The Situation in Biological Science*, 405. Moscow.
YUDKIN, J.
   1938. *Biol. Rev.*, **13**, 93.
ZALOKAR, M.
   1948. *Proc. Nat. Ac. Sci.*, **34**, 32.

APPENDIX

SOME STRUCTURAL FORMULAE

α-amino-acids (*see also* Figs. 1, 2, and 6)

Glycine $NH_2—CH_2—COOH$

Alanine $CH_3—CH—COOH$
$|$
NH_2

Serine $HO—CH_2—CH—COOH$
$|$
NH_2

Threonine $CH_3—CH—CH—COOH$
$OH\ \ NH_2$

Valine $(CH_3)_2CH—CH—COOH$
$|$
NH_2

Leucine
$(CH_3)_2CH—CH_2—CH—COOH$
$|$
NH_2

Isoleucine
$(CH_3)(C_2H_5)CH—CH—COOH$
$|$
NH_2

Aspartic acid
$HOOC—CH_2—CH—COOH$
$|$
NH_2

Glutamic acid
$HOOC—(CH_2)_2—CH—COOH$
$|$
NH_2

Proline $CH_2—CH—COOH$
$CH_2|$
$CH_2—NH$

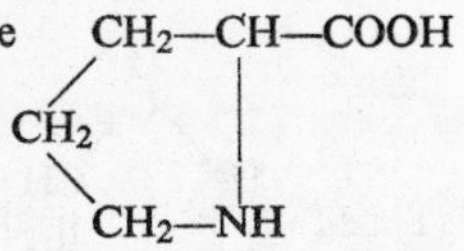

Ornithine
$NH_2(CH_2)_3—CH—COOH$
$|$
NH_2

Citrulline
$H_2N—CO—NH—(CH_2)_3—CH—COOH$
$|$
NH_2

Arginine
NH
$\|$
$H_2N—C—NH—(CH_2)_3—CH—COO$
$|$
NH_2

Canavanine
NH
$\|$
$H_2N—C—NH—O—(CH_2)_2—CH—COOH$
$|$
NH_2

Lysine $H_2N(CH_2)_4—CH—COOH$
$|$
NH_2

Phenylalanine

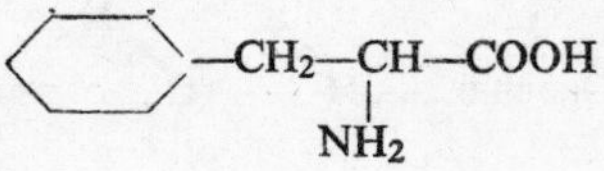

$—CH_2—CH—COOH$
$|$
NH_2

Tyrosine

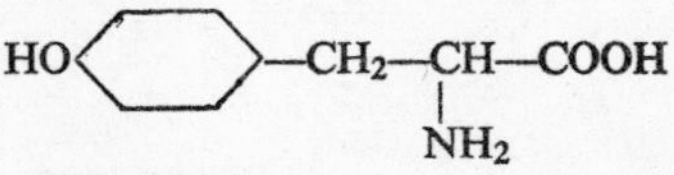

HO $—CH_2—CH—COOH$
$|$
NH_2

Tryptophan

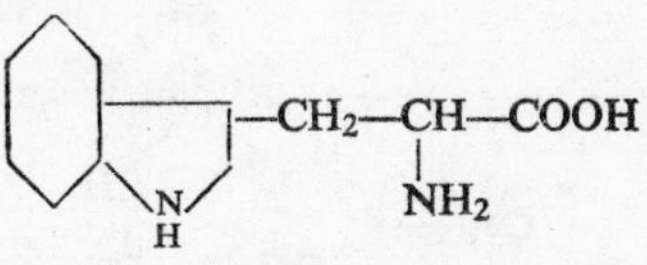

$—CH_2—CH—COOH$
$|$
NH_2

Cysteine $HS—CH_2—CH—COOH$
$|$
NH_2

Cystine $HOOC—CH—CH_2—S—S—CH_2—CH—COOH$

                           NH_2 NH_2

Methionine $H_3C—S—(CH_2)_2—CH—COOH$

                                  NH_2

RELATED COMPOUNDS

α-keto-acids $R—CO—COOH$

α-amino-adipic acid $HOOC—(CH_2)_3—CH—COOH$

                                      NH_2

α-keto-adipic acid $HOOC—(CH_2)_3—CO—COOH$

PURINE BASES AND THEIR DERIVATIVES

Adenine

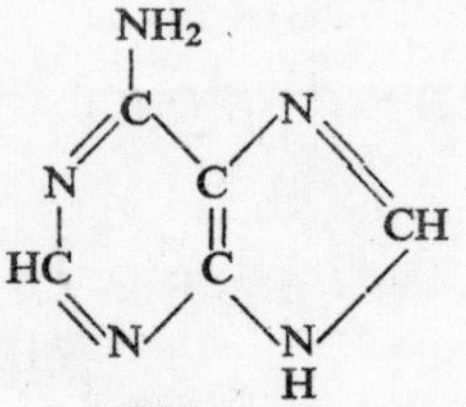

Uric acid

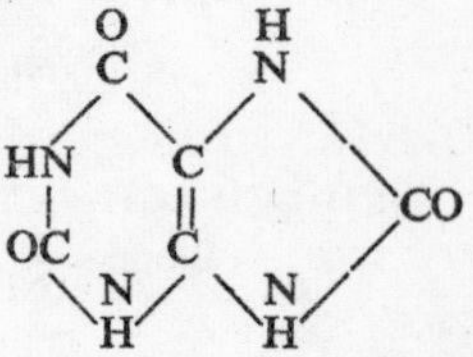

Guanine

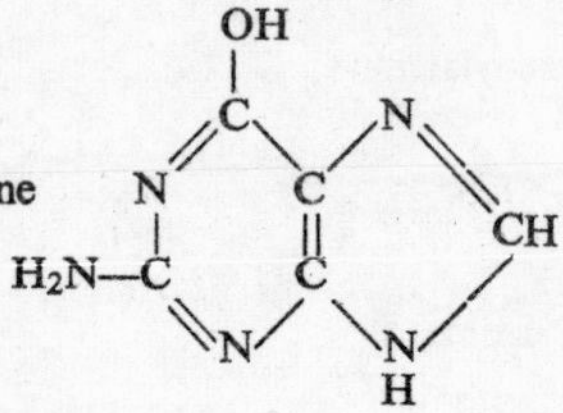

Allantoin

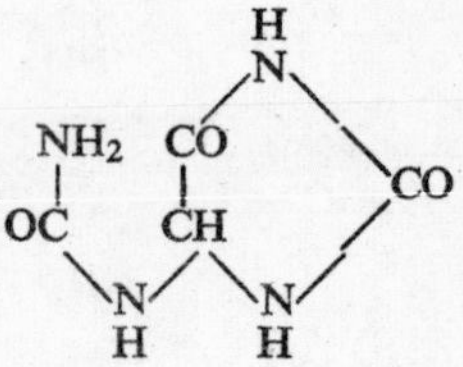

PYRIMIDINE BASES AND RELATED COMPOUNDS

Cytosine

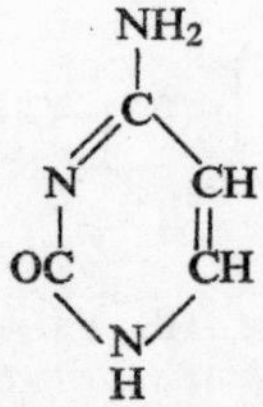

Uracil

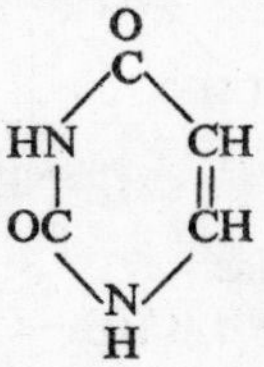

Thymine

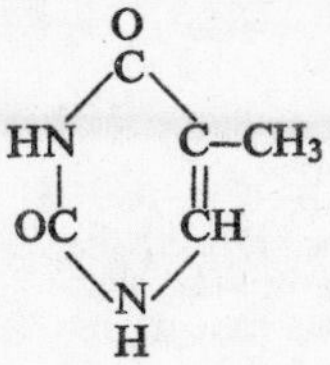

Orotic acid

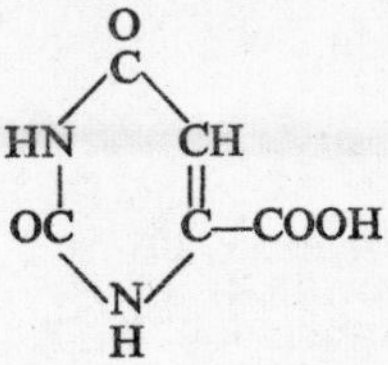

Thiamine (as a cation)

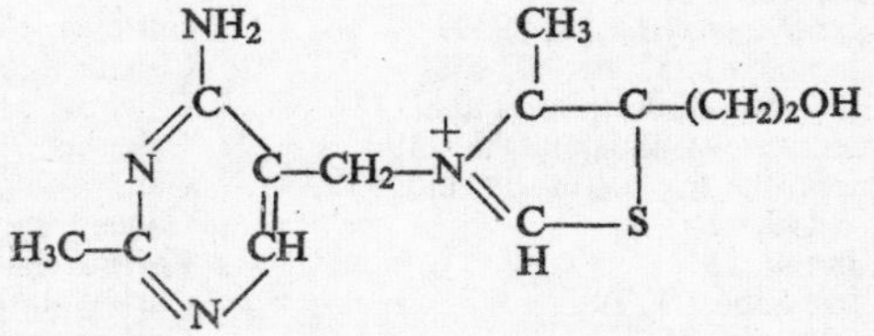

OTHER VITAMINS AND RELATED COMPOUNDS

Biotin

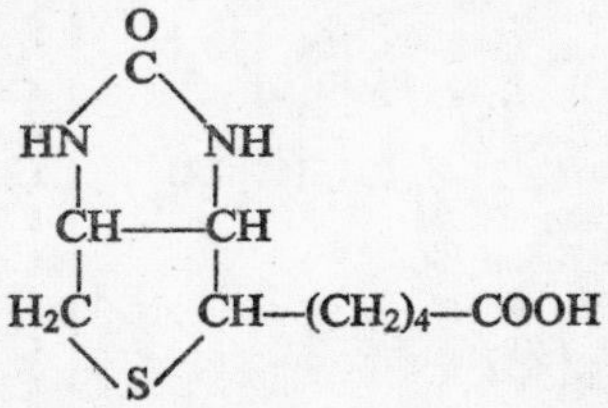

7-8-diamino-pelargonic acid

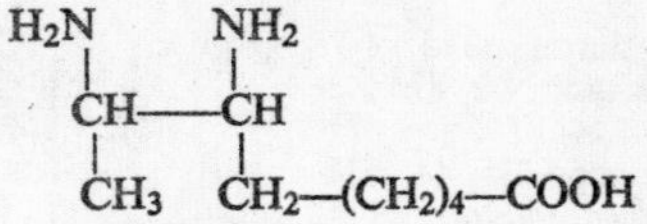

Pantothenic acid $HO-CH_2-C(CH_3)(CH_3)-CH(OH)-CO-NH-(CH_2)_2-COOH$

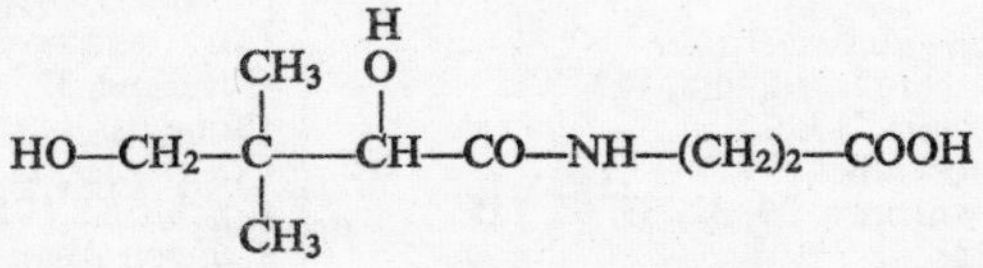

Pantoyl lactone

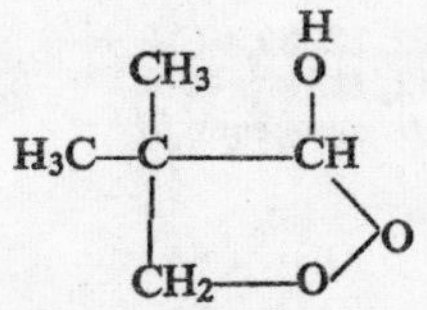

β-alanine $H_2N-(CH_2)_2-COOH$

Index